MACHINE SEE,
MACHINE DO

MACHINE SEE, MACHINE DO

HOW TECHNOLOGY MIRRORS BIAS IN OUR CRIMINAL JUSTICE SYSTEM

PATRICK K. LIN

NEW DEGREE PRESS

MACHINE SEE, MACHINE DO

How Technology Mirrors Bias in Our Criminal Justice System

ISBN	978-1-63730-821-9	*Paperback*
	978-1-63730-883-7	*Kindle Ebook*
	978-1-63730-967-4	*Ebook*

"Whether AI will help us reach our aspirations or reinforce the unjust inequalities is ultimately up to us."

— JOY BUOLAMWINI

Contents

For every person who has ever been shortchanged, excluded, and underestimated by machines.

For the public interest technologists improving the world with their hope, vision, and perseverance.

For the activists and advocates protecting civil liberties through organizing, education, and dedication.

Introduction

———

Much of what New York City looks like today is attributed to a man who never held elected office or received any formal training in architecture or urban planning.

Robert Moses has been called the "master builder" of mid-twentieth century New York and its surrounding suburbs. He shaped much of the infrastructure of modern New York City, Long Island, Rockland County, and Westchester County (Caro, 1974).

Over the course of his forty-four-year career, Moses built nearly seven hundred miles of road, including massive highways that stretched out of Manhattan into Long Island and Upstate New York; twenty thousand acres of parkland and public beaches; 658 playgrounds; seven new bridges; the UN Headquarters; the Central Park Zoo; and the Lincoln Center for the Performing Arts (Burkeman, 2015). It would be an understatement to say Moses left a lasting mark on New York. "In the twentieth century, the influence of Robert Moses on the cities of America was greater than that of any other person," wrote American historian Lewis Mumford.

However, new, large-scale developments come with a price—and not everyone pays the same amount.

To build hundreds of miles of highways and dozens of housing and urban renewal projects, Moses had more than five hundred thousand people evicted (Gratz, 2007). Black and Brown people comprised 40 percent of the evicted population at a time when those demographics made up only about 10 percent of the New York City's overall population (Census Bureau, 2021). The construction of Lincoln Center alone displaced more than seven thousand working-class families and eight hundred businesses. Many of these evicted New Yorkers ended up in Harlem and the Bronx, further segregating the city (Williams, 2017). Moses also avoided building public pools in Black neighborhoods and instead designed those same neighborhoods to be prone to traffic congestion, not only withholding public goods from Black neighborhoods, but also forcing them to bear the brunt of the social costs (Schindler, 2015).

Robert Moses with a model of the proposed Battery Bridge.
Source: The Library of Congress.

Moses infamously hated the idea of poor people—particularly poor people of color—using the new public parks and beaches he was building on Long Island (Burkeman, 2015). To that end, Moses used his influence and connections to pass a law forbidding public buses on highways, but he knew laws could someday be repealed. "Legislation can always be changed," Moses said. "It's very hard to tear down a bridge once it's up." So Moses built scores of bridges that were too low to let public buses pass, "literally concretizing discrimination" (Bornstein, 2017). The effect of these decisions has been profound and enduring. Decades later, the bus laws Moses fought for were overturned. Still, the towns he built along the highways remain as segregated as ever.

People often do not want to believe seemingly innocuous objects—like bridges or highways—can be racial or political, but as Moses' buildings and plans show, human history is inherently racial and political. Moses' racist views played out in what he built, how he built, and where he built.

But Moses was not alone. He wielded tremendous power and influence throughout his career, but he was still just an individual operating within a system built on bias and racism. For example, the Federal Housing Administration's *Underwriting Manual* states "incompatible racial groups should not be permitted to live in the same communities," recommending highways be built as a way to separate Black neighborhoods from white neighborhoods (Gross, 2017). Rooting out bias isn't only about powerful individuals; it isn't even just about you or me. It's about history and systems that continue to exist, bridges that are too difficult to tear down.

Discriminatory decisions and policies of the past impact the present. Racial and social inequity affect the very fabric of our reality. Everything has costs and benefits, and these are not evenly distributed. The decision, whether conscious or unconscious, to advance or burden some members of society over others is fundamentally racial and political.

Artificial intelligence is no different. The technology is relentlessly improving and increasingly pervasive, yet despite well-documented biases, AI developed in the private and public sectors alike consistently fail to account for it. Somehow, in the past two decades, we got the idea machines make better decisions than humans. We began saying things like, "People are biased, but AI will be more objective." We have forgotten humans design and deploy AI to serve their purposes. Humans, even those with the best intentions, can introduce bias to the AI they develop. Technology is not inherently objective or fair.

Today's technology, built from yesterday's data, will reflect the biased environment from which that data came. Bias often appears in AI systems through factors like race and gender, which generally are not directly inputted into the system but still have a strong influence over the system's decisions. The system is especially prone to bias when one of these factors is strongly correlated with information directly used by the system.

For example, suppose a system that makes determinations about someone's level of education uses zip code as a factor to make its decisions. Direct information about race is never given to the system, so how can a system like that be biased?

"Zip code is correlated with race since a lot of neighborhoods in America are still segregated," senior staff technologist Daniel Kahn Gillmor at the ACLU's Speech, Privacy, and Technology Project said to me. Gillmor's work focuses on the way our technical infrastructure shapes society and impacts civil liberties. "The data you're using to make these guesses is ultimately going to be pulled from a society that has a bunch of other problems, and the system is going to just reflect those problems back."

By using zip code as a factor, the AI system is indirectly making decisions based on race. In other words, zip code is a proxy for race. Therefore, even if the system's math and logic is all correct, an underlying ethical question reveals itself: is it appropriate to make these decisions based on these inputs?

A magical machine offering the promise of objectivity and fairness is extremely appealing. The public can be tricked into accepting an imperfect or even incompetent algorithm, particularly when the current state of an institution has historically been plagued by prejudice and bias, like the judicial system. We know things need to change and we want to believe technology can be that change. However, unlike humans, an algorithm cannot dissent, disobey, or make exceptions. People, on the other hand, can learn to account for ways in which data is a representation of the past.

So a question at the center of algorithmic fairness is whether an algorithm can be designed to comprehend the social and historical context of the data it relies on. Machines that cannot understand context will merely pass on institutionalized biases. To borrow a computer science adage: "bias in, bias out."

Algorithms pervade our lives today. However, the development and deployment of AI is virtually unregulated. Nowhere is this lack of regulation more problematic than in the criminal justice system, where AI directs the policing of our streets, surveils our citizens, and determines whether people should go to jail.

From my independent research and experiences at organizations like the Legal Aid Society's DNA Unit and the ACLU's Speech, Privacy, and Technology Project, I have seen time and time again how our institutions have relied more and more on automating justice to the detriment of our civil liberties.

Over time, something became clear to me: AI isn't going to take over the world, at least not in the *Terminator*-style apocalypse we might think. Instead, if we are not careful, AI will take all our human mistakes and immortalize them. Fixing the technology is just one part of the solution. Ultimately, we need to fix our systems and institutions. We need to think critically about the way humans use AI on other humans.

Despite the hallowed way people have used words like "algorithm" and "AI," almost every aspect of such decision-making is ultimately left to humans. Algorithms are designed by humans and run on computers built by humans. Algorithms are trained on data created and collected by humans. Algorithms are evaluated based on how well they reflect human priorities and values.

Plenty of literature on AI focuses on how the technology is flawed and how algorithmic bias must be addressed. I want to focus on the human aspect of this technology: the people who design and deploy AI and the history of how it came to be. I believe fixing bias in AI is about changing the way humans treat other humans.

My goal is to provide a new perspective on how to tackle this fascinating, complex, and important problem which exists at the intersection of the future of technology and our civil liberties. For those just starting to learn about AI and algorithmic bias, I hope this book can be an approachable guide to this space.

We need to think critically about how some of the same technology that has made our lives more convenient has also been used in unexpected, invasive, and cruel ways, especially on human lives who are historically neglected, marginalized, and victimized. We cannot expect simple and elegant solutions to these messy and complicated problems. Machines inherit our views and our history, including our prejudices and biases.

For policymakers, I hope this book shows just how lawless the realm of AI is, particularly as it pertains to criminal justice. It is no secret law and policy have failed to keep pace with technological advances. However, losing this race will diminish our individual rights.

This technology is making decisions that have profound ramifications, placing more people in the crosshairs of the police, and mislabeling people as criminals for factors they have no control over. I also highlight potential solutions and provide a more complete understanding of how law and policy can begin to right some of these wrongs and prevent future harm.

For AI developers and software engineers, I hope this book emphasizes how crucial your role is in both the problem and the solution to algorithmic bias. As AI evolves, your role shifts further from developer or engineer—and closer to policymaker. The lines of code you are writing and the products you are creating affect real-life people. It is important to recognize how that impact will vary for each person. Law and policy are just one piece of the puzzle. The way we build our technology must also change.

Ultimately, we need to ensure these processes do not lose their humanity. Our government's once *individualized* forms of surveillance have become *mass* surveillance. Our police and courts are turning to machines to make significant, life-altering decisions. We've long given up the idea justice is blind. It's about time we give up the idea technology is blind too.

AI is not some kind of silver bullet. We cannot rely solely on machines to solve problems created by humans. When autopilot was developed, we did not send passengers on airplanes without pilots in the cockpit. Similarly, we cannot completely remove human perspective or interaction from processes like policing and criminal justice, processes that have immense human impact. Machines are not a substitute for community engagement and holistic crime reduction measures.

Ironically (and tragically), the human obsession with predicting the future results in technology recreating the past—and its mistakes. The past cannot be rewritten, but one way or another, the response to AI in surveillance and criminal justice will determine whether hard-won civil liberties endure or become forgotten relics.

PART 1:

GHOST IN THE MACHINE

CHAPTER 1

Franglen's Monster

"Pray, Mr. Babbage, if you put into the machine wrong figures, will the right answers come out?"
— CHARLES BABBAGE, DESIGNER OF THE ANALYTICAL ENGINE, A PROTOTYPE OF THE FIRST COMPUTER

I've loved science fiction movies since I first watched C-3PO awkwardly shuffle through the sterile, white hallways of a spaceship in *Star Wars: Episode IV – A New Hope* (1977). I was especially fascinated by movie depictions of AI and its relationship with human characters. AI and its advancements may have become a popular topic in recent years, but AI has been a focal point for filmmakers for nearly a century (Tomlinson, 2018).

AI's first onscreen appearance was in the 1927 German expressionist movie *Metropolis,* in which a humanoid robot wreaks havoc in the titular city. Not a great first impression for AI, I'll admit. Although the first AI to appear in an American movie wouldn't be for another twenty-four years, the portrayal was noticeably more positive. Gort from the 1951 movie *The Day the Earth Stood Still* was a silent guardian to the movie's protagonist.

In 1968, HAL 9000 from *2001: A Space Odyssey* was the main antagonist but was far more human than any other movie robot before him, despite being a fixture with no body. In 1983's *WarGames*, it was the first depiction of AI's involvement in a nonfictional war. A year later, *The Terminator* gave us "Skynet," and to this day, "Skynet" is a commonly used analogy for the threat posed by advanced AI.

In 1999, *The Matrix* graced us with some of the most stylish visual effects and fight choreography ever committed to film, as well as a quintessential Hollywood vision of what an AI takeover would look like. *Avengers: Age of Ultron* came out in 2015 and became the highest grossing movie with AI at the center.

AI has remained such a popular subject in movies because it forces us to reflect on what humanity is. *Blade Runner* (1982)—one of my all-time favorite movies—*Her* (2013), and *Ex Machina* (2014) are just some movies that challenge audiences to question what being human really means and where we draw the line in a world where advanced AI is possible.

The public is increasingly aware of the ubiquity of AI and its concepts, particularly the elusive algorithm. Introduced in 2004, Google Search's autocomplete algorithm predicts your search based on your past searches and what other people are searching for. Algorithms determine your creditworthiness and help banks decide whether to lend you money or not. Facebook and Instagram use algorithms to predict what ads appear on your feed. Insurance companies use algorithms to predict your likelihood of being in an accident or getting sick. Netflix and Spotify collect data on your genre preferences and rely on an algorithm to suggest new shows or songs to you. Algorithms are everywhere, and in some ways, they make things faster, easier, and more curated.

However, algorithms are also used to determine which neighborhoods police officers patrol. They make decisions about immigration status. They predict the likelihood of an individual committing another crime. Algorithms are currently used in courtrooms to determine whether someone goes to jail or not.

I believe the explosion of algorithms in our public institutions are the result of our discomfort with uncertainty.

From time immemorial, humankind has been obsessed with predicting the future. From oracles' prophecies of Greek antiquity to financial models on Wall Street, we have tried to peer into the future. Humanity has always been uncomfortable with, even scared of, uncertainty. We want to know what is to come so we can control it. We created machines and asked them to be fortunetellers.

For a long time now, financial institutions have been relying on algorithms to gauge someone's creditworthiness and ability to pay off loans. US Immigration and Customs Enforcement (ICE) recently abandoned its Extreme Vetting Initiative, which partnered with tech companies to analyze immigrants' social media activity to predict if they would become a terrorist (Funk, 2019). AI is also used to predict crime and analyze forensic evidence.

However, prediction works like a mirror.

In the 1970s, Dr. Geoffrey Franglen, the vice dean and an admissions assessor at St. George's Hospital Medical School in London, started working on a computer program to screen student applications for admission (Schwartz, 2019). Franglen's main motivation was to make the admissions process more efficient, but he also hoped to eliminate inconsistencies in the way the admissions staff evaluated applications. The idea was by leaving this task to a technical system, all student applicants would be subject to exactly the same evaluation, therefore creating a more fair process.

The algorithm did just the opposite.

Franglen's algorithm was used for the first time in 1979. That year, student applications were reviewed by both the computer and human assessors. Franglen found his algorithm agreed with the selection panel's decision 90 to 95 percent of the time. For the medical school's administration, this outcome was proof the algorithm could replace the human assessors. By 1982, all applications to St. George's were screened by Franglen's algorithm.

After a few years, some staff members expressed concern about the lack of diversity among successful applicants. While conducting a review of Franglen's algorithm, they noticed certain rules in the algorithm evaluated applicants on the basis of apparently irrelevant factors, such as place of birth and name.

In 1988, the UK Commission for Racial Equality found St. George's guilty of discrimination. Franglen's algorithm classified candidates as "Caucasian" or "non-Caucasian" on the basis of their names and places of birth. If applicants had non-Caucasian names, the selection process was weighed against them. The algorithm was also found to be biased against women.

The Commission concluded the problem at the medical school was not only *technical*, but also *cultural*.

Many staff members viewed the admissions machine as unquestionable and therefore did not take the time to ask how it distinguished between students. At a deeper level, the algorithm was sustaining the biases that already existed in the admissions process. After all, Franglen tested the algorithm against its human counterparts and found a 90 to 95 percent correlation of outcomes. However, by codifying the school's discriminatory practices into an algorithm, he was ensuring these biases would be replayed in perpetuity.

When left unchecked, a racially unequal past will necessarily produce racially unequal outputs.

Over three decades later, algorithms have become significantly more complex, yet we continue to face the same challenges. AI can certainly help identify and reduce the impact of human biases, but it can also make the problem worse by baking in and deploying biases at scale in sensitive application areas.

Indeed, as algorithmic decision-making systems are increasingly rolled out into high-stakes domains—like hiring, housing, health care, and criminal justice—the perpetuation and amplification of existing social biases based on historical data has become an enormous concern. For instance, investigative newsroom ProPublica found a criminal risk assessment algorithm used in Broward County, Florida, mislabeled Black defendants as "high risk" at nearly twice the rate it mislabeled white defendants (Angwin et al., 2016).

Instead of predicting the future, algorithms are a self-fulfilling prophecy.

But how is this happening, and why? Before we can begin to answer these questions, we first need to understand the terminology being used. Algorithm, machine learning, and artificial intelligence are often lumped together, leading to confusion about what each term means. Understanding the distinctions will clarify how bias makes its way into this technology.

ALGORITHM

An algorithm is a series of instructions that are followed step by step to complete a task or solve a problem. For example, a cake recipe can be thought of as an algorithm for baking a cake. Most algorithms are simpler than most people think. In fact, they can be as simple as a single if-then statement. *If this happens, then that will happen.*

On the other hand, algorithms can also be a sequence of complex mathematical equations. An algorithm's complexity can be boiled down to either how complicated each step is or simply the sheer number of steps the algorithm needs to execute.

Computer algorithms first rose to prominence in the mid-twentieth century. They take an input and apply each step of the algorithm to that information to produce an output. For instance, a search engine like Google is an algorithm that takes a search query as an input and searches its database for items relevant to the words in the query. The search results are the output.

Nowadays, the main purpose of an algorithm is automation. By automatically performing a task, processes have become more efficient and machines are able to process more information with little to no human intervention.

"Algorithms are doing for mental work what the Industrial Revolution did for manual work," Pedro Domingos, a computer science professor at the University of Washington, told news website *Mashable*. "Algorithms are the automation of intelligence. And if you think about that, this is a very powerful thing: to do something that used to take, you know, human thinking and labor to do now can be done by an algorithm" (Kraus, 2020).

MACHINE LEARNING

The most sophisticated algorithms use machine learning, a type of artificial intelligence. Traditional programming requires a human being to write the algorithm, which can be time-consuming and costly, especially when a complex algorithm is involved. "Machine learning is the computer discovering its own algorithms instead of being told what to do," Domingos said.

Machine learning algorithms are "trained" to identify patterns in massive amounts of data, allowing them to learn from new information and improve their accuracy over time without being programmed to do so. Training data is an extremely large dataset used to teach a machine learning model to identify said patterns. Ultimately, this allows algorithms to make decisions and predictions based on new data. This data can be numbers, words, images, whatever. If the data can be digitally stored, then it can be fed into a machine learning algorithm. The better the algorithm, the more accurate the decisions and predictions will become as it takes in more data.

More likely than not, you have interacted with machine learning in some way. Both Netflix and YouTube use machine learning to recommend shows and videos. Similarly, Facebook and Twitter use machine learning to determine what content should appear on your feed. Each of these platforms is collecting as much data about you as possible—what genres you frequently watch and what content you engage with the most—and using machine learning to predict what you want next. In other words, the computer finds a pattern, then applies the pattern. The machine is, well, learning.

ARTIFICIAL INTELLIGENCE

Lastly, we have artificial intelligence, generally shortened to AI, which might just be one of the most misunderstood concepts of our time. Unfortunately, those Sci-Fi movies I love have only made the concept more complicated. Often when we think about AI, we think about Terminator robots or Ultron facing off against the Avengers.

Movies aren't the only ones to blame, though. Part of the problem is the lack of a standardized definition. Alan Turing is generally credited with the origin of the concept of AI when he speculated in 1950 about "thinking machines" that could reason at the level of a human being (Sharkey, 2012). A few years later, John McCarthy coined the term "artificial intelligence" to refer to machines that could think autonomously (Myers, 2011). Since the 1950s, scientists have disagreed on what constitutes "thinking" and "intelligence."

In the broadest sense, AI refers to machines capable of learning, reasoning, and acting for themselves. AI systems can make their own decisions when given new information, imitating intelligent human behavior (Hao, 2018). What sets AI apart from more analog machines, which are only capable of mechanical or predetermined responses, is AI algorithms are designed to make decisions based on data it is provided.

The problem with prediction is, without thoughtful intervention, it is doomed to simply repeat history (Mayson, 2019). One of the most important challenges facing AI is figuring out how to account for all the historical, social, and racial baggage that comes with the data AI being used to make decisions. Information that is processed by AI should be unbiased and nondiscriminatory; otherwise, AI algorithms will be unfair and unjust, just like Franglen's.

As a result, developers of AI are frequently placed in precarious positions where they decide what values are important to a community. Today, AI developers are asked to design software that will predict criminality, determine which streets get surveilled, and whether someone should be released from prison. When balancing competing interests—efficiency, accuracy, equity, and justice—something's got to give. Overzealously automating decision-making processes can leave out any nuance or opportunity for exceptions.

"There has been so much focus on efficiency when it comes to developing new technologies, but efficiency is really about maximizing value while reducing the time and effort spent on a particular process," said Juyoun Han, a lawyer at New York City law firm Eisenberg & Baum.

Han is the partner leading the law firm's Artificial Intelligence Fairness & Data Privacy practice. "When the goal is sustainability, efficiency may not be the best way to get there. I think we benefit from creating systems that are well-thought-out, that are meticulously examined and scrutinized. There is a trade-off when we prioritize efficiency."

AI is generally thought of as getting smarter over time. What is often overlooked is the human aspect in this narrative: humans design, train, and deploy this technology.

While it may be exciting to get swept up by the idea of intelligent machines that have no need for human input, the truth is AI is only as good as we are.

CHAPTER 2

Automating Bias

———

"The future is made of the same stuff as the present."

— SIMONE WEIL

I love technology. I have vivid memories of playing computer games on the 1999 lineup of iMac G3 computers. Even when the computer wasn't turned on, I was captivated by the hardware inside of the forty-pound, egg-shaped personal computer, which was visible due to its translucent "Bondi Blue" colored plastic case. In middle school, I spent my afternoons at robotics club, tinkering with motors and sensors. For as long as I can remember, I have been fascinated by technology, especially how quickly new features or capabilities were introduced and how technology made our lives more convenient.

Having grown up when technology became more accessible to households and being privileged enough to afford some of this technology growing up, my lived experiences may predispose me to having a more favorable opinion on technology. I would even say I'm *biased* as a result of these experiences.

"Bias" often has a negative connotation, but it's important to recognize it's a natural phenomenon. After all, our brains are constantly forming associations to make sense of the world more effectively and efficiently around us.

Psychologists have defined and classified more than 180 cognitive biases (Yagoda, 2018). Cognitive bias is understood to be a tendency, inclination, or prejudice toward or against something or someone. It includes a variety of processes that may lead to inaccurate judgments or interpretations. Bias can also affect memory, reasoning, and decision-making (Tversky and Kahneman, 1974).

People aren't necessarily "bad" simply for harboring biases. However, the key is to be aware of your biases, check them, and adjust accordingly.

I think bias generally manifests in two forms.

Explicit bias, also known as conscious bias, is when a person is very clear about their feelings and attitudes toward certain groups. Behaviors motivated by explicit bias are conducted with intent. Explicit bias can be as overt as physical or verbal harassment or as subtle as exclusion.

Implicit or unconscious bias refers to how the human brain can take shortcuts when processing information. While these shortcuts may help us save time when making decisions, an unconscious bias is also a systematic thinking error that can cloud our judgment and ultimately impact our decisions (Papillon, 2021). For example, people who support a particular issue will not only seek information to support it, but will also interpret news stories in a way that upholds their existing ideas. This is also known as confirmation bias.

When I spoke to Gillmor, a technologist in the ACLU's Speech, Privacy, and Technology Project, he told me about how his friend could not get the water faucet in a public bathroom to turn on because her dark skin would not trigger the faucet sensors. "It was expecting a light reflection her skin didn't produce," Gillmor said. "She could wave a paper towel under the faucet and it would start, but her own skin wouldn't turn on the faucet."

Gillmor attributed this undesirable outcome to the faucet designers' unconscious biases. The designers most likely didn't do this on purpose, but they failed to use a complete range of complexions when training the faucet's sensors. Thus, the faucet worked fine for individuals with lighter skin, but would not register darker skin. According to Gillmor, underlying societal biases make their way into technology design, resulting in technology that is not going to work the same way for everyone.

Because implicit bias operates outside of a person's awareness, it can be in direct contradiction to that person's espoused beliefs and values. The danger of implicit bias is it automatically seeps into a person's affect or behavior.

But how does bias affect algorithms?

Algorithmic bias occurs when an algorithmic decision creates unfair outcomes that unjustifiably and arbitrarily advantage or disadvantage certain groups. According to the

Algorithmic Justice League, an organization that combines art and research to inform the public about the social implications and harms of AI, algorithmic bias can encode racism, sexism, ableism, and other forms of harmful discrimination into machines (Algorithmic Justice League, 2021).

From facial recognition to your phone's virtual assistant, tools rely on AI systems that learn by analyzing massive amounts of data. This system of learning is not unlike the way the human brain works, earning the name "neural network." If an algorithm is a series of instructions, then a neural network is a series of algorithms designed to recognize underlying relationships in a dataset.

With respect to algorithmic bias, I tend to associate unconscious bias with the design and development stages of the algorithm. Design choices or how AI is trained can be the result of accidental biases. AI-enabled hiring tools, for example, may be designed with the genuine goal of reducing human bias from a process that boils down to judging and evaluating a stranger. Maybe the hiring tool is designed to record a video of someone responding to interview prompts then comparing credentials, experiences, or interview responses to the highest performing employees at a company.

This whole design process may be totally void of any intention of biasing certain candidates. Still, a hiring tool that assesses candidates' facial movement and voice may discriminate against people with disabilities that affect facial expression and speech patterns. Similarly, customizing the tool to identify an employer's preferred traits based on the employer's existing pool of employees leads to a host of problems as well. If people of color are historically underrepresented in an industry or company, then the hiring tool will learn to simply screen out people of color, essentially treating under-represented traits as undesired, automating exclusion.

On the other hand, I think of conscious bias as being hand in hand with how algorithms are used, or decisions about how they are used. For instance, if law enforcement agencies are choosing to use technology on specific demographics—generally poor people of color—that is conscious bias in action. Throughout history, policymakers have also made conscious decisions to target, disenfranchise, and harm activists and minority communities.

Humans and algorithms alike learn from the past. As a result, predictions about an individual or community is anchored in the historical behavior of similar individuals or communities.

In many discussions about how bias creeps into AI, the blame falls on biased training data. While biased training data should definitely take some of the blame, reality is more complicated.

Bias can be introduced before any data has even been collected. Before any lines of code are written, corporations, government agencies, and computer scientists must ask two questions: "what problem are we trying to solve?" and "what is the purpose of this algorithm?" Answers to these questions will guide virtually every future decision.

For example, a bank would be interested in predicting a customer's creditworthiness, but this metric is vague. To quantify and translate it into something that can be stored as data, the bank must make a decision: maximize its profit margins or maximize the number of loans that get repaid. The problem is "those decisions are made for various business reasons other than fairness or discrimination," Solon Barocas, a Cornell University professor who specializes in fairness in machine learning, told the MIT *Technology Review* (Hao, 2019). If the algorithm learned giving out subprime loans was an effective way to maximize profit, it would end up engaging in predatory behavior—even if that wasn't the company's intention.

Moving onto the data collection stage, institutions and programmers must ask two new questions: "is the data representative of the population this algorithm will be used on?" and "how might this data reflect historical prejudices?"

Gillmor's water faucet example demonstrates how data that is unrepresentative of the real world can cause technology to fail. Another is when machine learning algorithms are fed more photos of light-skinned faces than dark-skinned faces. The resulting facial recognition system would inevitably be worse at recognizing darker-skinned faces. The earlier discussion about hiring tools is another example of what happens when past information or existing prejudices will be replicated when they aren't accounted for.

In October 2018, Amazon scrapped its internal recruiting tool when it discovered it was dismissing female candidates. By training the hiring tool on historical hiring decisions, which favored men over women, the tool learned to do the same. Considering how male-dominated the tech industry is, Amazon surely is not the only company guilty of this.

That leads us to another key question: who is designing these algorithms?

"I'm not worried about machines taking over the world. I'm worried about groupthink, insularity, and arrogance in the AI community—especially with the current hype and demand for people in the field," wrote Timnit Gebru, a prominent AI researcher and Google's former AI ethics lead. "The people creating the technology are a big part of the system. If many are actively excluded from its creation, this technology will benefit a few while harming a great many."

In the United States, racial and ethnic lines are blurring and softening. The country is more diverse than it's ever been. Yet, after the 2020 primary elections, 97 percent of all Republican elected officials and 79 percent of all Democratic elected officials are white (Reflective Democracy Campaign, 2021). The composition of our government does not reflect the nation's current or growing diversity.

The private sector has similar problems. In 2015, Google Photos tagged two Black people as gorillas (Barr, 2015). In 2016, it was revealed LinkedIn's search engine showed a preference for male names (Day, 2016). That same year, Microsoft's AI chatbot, Tay, spent just one day learning from interactions on Twitter and began spouting anti-Semitic messages (Vincent, 2016). In September 2021, repeating Google's mistake, Facebook's AI-generated video prompts included a "primates" label on a video of Black men (Mac, 2021).

A 2019 report from the AI Now Institute at NYU found more than 80 percent of AI professors were men. At Facebook, only 15 percent of AI researchers were women. At Google, only 10 percent. The results were even worse for Black representation. Only 2.5 percent of Google's workforce was Black while Facebook and Microsoft were each at 4 percent (West, Whittaker, and Crawford, 2019).

But this isn't just about making an industry or institution more diverse for the sake of diversity. AI is not only here to stay; it's going to advance at breakneck speeds and play a progressively larger role in our day-to-day lives. Corporations are producing mass surveillance systems and forensic analysis algorithms. Government institutions are using these same tools to surveil, arrest, and imprison people. This lack of diversity in both the AI industry and government is concentrating an ever-increasing amount of power and capital in the hands of a select few.

It's a story as old as time.

"When new technology is developed, inequalities in society become more obvious. The people who come out as winners are always the same. So are the losers," said Han, an attorney specialized in AI fairness and data privacy. "We need to ask an important question when we choose to automate decision-making processes: who will benefit from this and who will be harmed by it?"

What may seem to be a one-off incident or a small-scale problem can quickly rise to systemic heights thanks to the ubiquity and scalability of AI. We've managed to outsource our biases to machines and built systems that automate the bias at a scale we've never been able to achieve before.

Still, AI is often depicted as a panacea that can fix the world's problems. Maybe it can, but it can also reinforce bias and exclusion, even when it is used with the best intentions (Buolamwini, 2018). Similarly, machine learning can produce powerful predictions, but its reliance on data collected from current biased systems and institutions will ensure today's problems are preserved for the future (Mayson, 2019).

The problem of bias doesn't stop at the technology, though. Technology in and of itself is not biased. Instead, it can amplify existing problems in the systems we've constructed. When I spoke with Aaron Horowitz, a computer scientist and chief data scientist at the ACLU, he told me algorithmic bias was just one piece of the puzzle. "Yes, there's bias, but algorithms are a mirror of society," he said. "A lot of the problems involve measurement choices, so they have more to do with the institutions than the algorithms themselves."

In other words, algorithmic bias is just a symptom. The root cause of bias in AI is us. Our biases and the institutions we've constructed—laws, police, justice—produce the problems we are seeing in our technology. We cannot overlook the human element of this issue. People design AI. People use AI. Most importantly, people choose how AI is used on other people.

PART 2:

AUTOMATING THE WATCHERS

CHAPTER 3

Lights, Camera, Surveillance!

———

"...something merciless that carried a printed list and a gun, that moved machine-like through the flat, bureaucratic job of killing. A thing without emotions, or even a face; a thing that if killed got replaced immediately by another resembling it. And so on, until everyone real and alive had been shot."

— PHILIP K. DICK, *DO ANDROIDS DREAM OF ELECTRIC SHEEP?*

Over seven decades after its publication, George Orwell's *1984* continues to provide us with the metaphor of choice for surveillance: "Big Brother." In fact, a 2014 study conducted by PEN America found in 120 blog posts and articles about surveillance, "1984" was the only literary metaphor used (Olukotun, 2014). However, as surveillance technology becomes increasingly sophisticated, it also outpaces public understanding of the threats it poses. *1984's* Big Brother does not fully capture our reality: the effects of the surveillance state are not felt equally by all citizens but are instead felt more harshly by vulnerable and marginalized people.

A more nuanced and prophetic depiction can be found in Philip K. Dick's *Do Androids Dream of Electric Sheep?*, perhaps more popularly known for its movie adaptation, *Blade Runner*. The book renders a "bureaucratic machinery of terror" that looks uncomfortably familiar in the age of police brutality, Black Lives Matter, and the ever-growing surveillance capabilities of law enforcement (Berlatsky, 2017). Although Rick Deckard, a policeman who hunts and kills androids, is the protagonist, his portrayal in the book underscores Dick's discomfort with the police's license to kill, as well as their discriminatory use of that license.

The police in Dick's novel are cruel and unrelenting killers. While the androids in the movie have superhuman strength and reflexes, in the book, they are vulnerable victims. Deckard also isn't one of "a few bad apples" spoiling a righteous police force, nor is he a just man stuck in an unjust system. Instead, Deckard is an unremarkable man doing an unremarkable job. He's just a relatively insignificant part of a larger machine, a machine that takes part in selective violence aimed at a marginalized minority.

Although metaphors can be helpful—and I am partial to *Do Androids Dream of Electric Sheep?*—I also recognize metaphors can distract from the fact real lives are affected by them. When I first read the book, I was drawn into the post-nuclear-apocalyptic world and the complicated relationships between humankind and machines. However, we need not look to science fiction to find examples of the disproportionate surveilling of marginalized groups.

After all, this is not a new phenomenon.

In eighteenth-century New York City, lantern laws required Black, mixed race, and Indigenous enslaved people to carry candle lanterns after dark to be publicly visible. The law carried several punishments for individuals in violation of these lantern laws, including public flogging of up to forty lashes. Every white person was deputized to stop enslaved people who walked without the supervisory device at night (Garcia-Rojas, 2016).

The ghost of lantern laws has lived on in modern-day police practices and surveillance technology. In 2011, at the height of the stop-and-frisk program, the New York Police Department stopped nearly seven hundred thousand people. Since 2002, nine out of ten stopped-and-frisked New Yorkers have been completely innocent. Although stop-and-frisk was largely undone by public outrage and legal challenges, to this day, 90 percent of all people stopped are Black or Latinx (NYCLU, 2019).

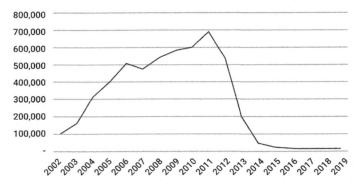

Number of NYPD-Reported Stops by Year

In 2014, just as New York's stop-and-frisk program was being rolled back, massive floodlights with NYPD insignias cropped up in historically overpoliced neighborhoods, particularly affordable housing developments. A 2014 *Vice* article described these floodlights as "creating the eerie look of a perpetual crime scene" (Surico, 2014). This is part of the NYPD's strategy, known as Omnipresence (yes, the name is extremely on the nose and just as terrifying).

Omnipresence highlights a trend toward less confrontational and more omnipresent methods of police surveillance and eavesdropping. As intrusive practices like stop-and-frisk declined, police departments turned to technology as constant sentries. There is something categorically distinct about today's surveillance technology: the extent to which it operates on a mass scale.

The lantern laws of the eighteenth century, and even the wiretapping and electronic eavesdropping that has taken place over the past 150 years, were highly individualized.

Individuals were required to carry lanterns. Individual phone conversations were being tapped. Today, with the help of big data and AI, our institutions can keep an eye on communities, cities, and the whole country.

In March 2015, the NYPD started employing ShotSpotter, a privately developed gunshot detection system that uses sensors to pick up sounds that appear to be gunshots. Audio snippets are sent to vendor employees, who attempt to verify whether the sound represents a gunshot, then information about the location of the sound is sent to ShotSpotter clients: police departments.

But if ShotSpotter is listening for and recording ambient noises, doesn't that mean it's always listening? Doesn't that mean it can listen in on conversations too?

Albert Fox Cahn confirmed those concerns when I asked him about surveillance technology used in major American cities. Cahn is the founder and executive director of the Surveillance Technology Oversight Project (S.T.O.P.), former fellow at the Engelberg Center on Innovation Law & Policy at NYU School of Law, and a visiting fellow at Yale Law School's Information Society Project. Cahn began S.T.O.P. because he believed emerging surveillance technologies pose an unprecedented threat to civil rights.

"ShotSpotter has a widely documented high error rate. On top of that, its directional microphones are only being placed in low-income communities of color, so those communities bear the entire cost of when the software gets it wrong," Cahn explained. "You essentially end up with an algorithm-driven version of stop-and-frisk."

Use of stop-and-frisk and technology like ShotSpotter is often associated with "broken windows" policing. Before criminologists George Kelling and James Q. Wilson introduced their broken windows theory in a 1982 article for *The Atlantic*, Stanford University psychologist Philip Zimbardo conducted an experiment testing the theory thirteen years earlier.

In 1969, Zimbardo arranged for a car to be parked in a Bronx neighborhood and a second car to be parked in Palo Alto, California. Both cars were left with no license plates and parked with their hoods up. After just ten minutes, "vandals" in the Bronx removed the radiator and battery. Within twenty-four hours, everything of value was stripped from the car and the car's windows were smashed.

Meanwhile, the car sitting in Palo Alto sat untouched for more than a week until Zimbardo himself, armed with a sledgehammer, smashed the car. After that, passersby quickly joined in, leaving the California car in a similar state as the New York car. What was Zimbardo's conclusion? "Conditions that create social inequality and put some people outside of the conventional reward structure of the society make them indifferent to its sanctions, laws, and implicit norms."

In response to the 1960s "race riots," Zimbardo set out to chronicle the social causes of vandalism to disprove the conservative argument that it is the result of individual or cultural pathology (Ansfield 2019). In a twist of fate, Zimbardo's experiment became the basis for one of the most influential, violent, and racialized theories of crime and policing in the United States.

Kelling and Wilson were intrigued by what happened to the abandoned cars in Zimbardo's study and, by distorting the study to serve their purposes, applied the findings on a larger scale: to entire communities. Using windows as a metaphor for disorder within neighborhoods, the two criminologists argued, "If a window in a building is broken and is left unrepaired, all the rest of the windows will soon be broken." Kelling and Wilson's theory linked low-level crime and disorder within a community to subsequent occurrences of serious crime.

In other words, they believed visible signs of disorder or decay—such as loitering, graffiti, prostitution, drug use, or subway fare evasion—can signal a neighborhood is uncared for. Kelling and Wilson thought if police departments addressed those problems, the bigger crimes wouldn't happen.

In an interview with *NPR*, Columbia University law professor Bernard Harcourt said Kelling and Wilson's argument came at an opportune time. "This was a period of high crime, and high incarceration, and it seemed there was no way out of that dynamic. It seemed as if there was no way out of just filling prisons to address the crime problem."

I don't think it's a coincidence the broken windows theory and tough-on-crime politics rose to prominence at around the same time. Throughout history, people in power have sought opportunities to distort trends and misrepresent facts to legitimize political agendas.

Before Kamala Harris became the first female vice president in US history, she dropped out of the presidential race in December 2019 after an onslaught of criticism from the left for her tough-on-crime record as district attorney of San Francisco and as California's attorney general.

A few years ago, that would have been unthinkable. Democrats and Republicans alike had historically favored tough-on-crime candidates. In the late 1960s, candidates began to campaign like they were competing for the "most draconian criminal justice policies" award. Richard Nixon won with his "law and order" campaign and, in June 1971, launched the war on drugs when he declared drug abuse to be "public enemy number one." Ronald Reagan greatly expanded the war on drugs by prioritizing criminal punishment over treatment, resulting in a massive increase in incarcerations for nonviolent drug offenses.

In 1988, George H. W. Bush won with notorious ads telling the story of Willie Horton, who was allowed out of prison under a weekend furlough program. Bill Clinton in 1992 bragged about supporting the death penalty and even took a break from his campaign so he could return to Arkansas to witness the execution of a mentally disabled man. In her 2014 reelection campaign for attorney general, Harris won over the endorsements of more than fifty law enforcement groups. She won by a landslide (Armour, 2019).

Politics fueled by fear of crime resulted in long-lasting, destructive social costs. Today, the US makes up less than

5 percent of the world's population, yet it has 20 percent of the world's incarcerated people (Wagner and Bertram, 2020). Historically marginalized and targeted groups, namely poor communities of color, bear the brunt: one out of every three Black boys born today can expect to go to prison in their lifetime, as can one of every six Latino boys—compare this to one of every seventeen white boys (NAACP, 2021).

I believe much of the surveillance technology deployed by police departments today, particularly those enabled by AI, is an outgrowth of this broken windows policing and history of tough-on-crime policies. Today's surveillance technology often focuses on lower-level infractions in the hopes of diminishing serious crimes. With the deployment of programs like Omnipresence and ShotSpotter, simply existing in a marginalized community seems to be reason for suspicion.

Brandon del Pozo is a postdoctoral researcher at Brown University who served nineteen years in the NYPD and four as the chief of police in Burlington, Vermont. When I spoke to him about how surveillance technology has changed policing, he agreed unchecked police surveillance manifests in unequal ways. "It doesn't so much criminalize new behaviors as it enforces laws against criminal behaviors in disparate or overbearing ways," del Pozo said. "We don't want to empower the police to enforce the law in ways that expand the reach, scope, and level of intrusion beyond anything we ever intended or believed was reasonable and necessary." He believes improving the quality of American policing lies in using the goals, methods, and metrics of public health to shape and guide its responses to both crime and non-criminal risk behaviors.

Kelling and Wilson may have introduced the broken windows theory, but William Bratton almost singlehandedly popularized broken windows policing policies across America. Bratton served as chief of the Los Angeles Police Department and commissioner of the Boston Police Department and the New York Police Department. His approach to policing can be summed up by a statement he made in 1994 after being appointed former New York City mayor Rudy Giuliani's police commissioner: "We are going to flush [homeless people] off the street in the same successful manner in which we flushed them out of the subway system" (Getlin and Rivera, 2015).

Bratton became the poster child of "the war against crime" in the 1990s by effectively translating the broken windows theory into aggressive policing practices. In New York City, he cracked down on panhandling, public drinking, and street prostitution. In Los Angeles, under his leadership, the LAPD issued thousands of tickets to homeless people for crimes of poverty, resulting in many being jailed for their inability to pay fines and fees.

In 2015, Bratton responded to police shootings and the rise of the Black Lives Matter movement by appearing on MSNBC's *Morning Joe* and citing assistant secretary of labor Daniel Patrick Moynihan's 1965 report, which argued America's Black communities were forced into a "tangle of pathology" that "seriously [inhibited] the progress of the group as a whole," with a particular focus on the plight of young Black men (Geary, 2015).

To put it another way, the Moynihan Report pushed the misconception poverty and crime were inherent features of Black communities; a misconception that shaped this nation's policing policies and wrapped a cloak of scientific legitimacy around the disproportionate punishment of young Black men in urban centers (Coates, 2015). The pseudo-statistical justifications outlined in Moynihan's report laid the groundwork for Bratton's CompStat (Comparative Statistics), an approach to crime reduction that uses computerized crime maps. Developed by the NYPD in 1994, the program maintained a database of crime statistics and police activity and mapped out that information to show where and when crimes were occurring.

In 2002, Bratton was named chief of the LAPD. At that point, CompStat was being adopted in other cities, including Los Angeles. However, according to Bratton, the LAPD version needed to be overhauled. In a paper he cowrote, Bratton asked, "How can we use predictive methods to create even more timely and successful intervention and crime reduction initiatives?" (Bratton and Malinowsky, 2008).

This question ultimately led Bratton to seek out researchers to take CompStat to the next stage of its evolution: predictive policing. History has shown us the effects of surveillance practices and technology are not felt equally by all members of our society. Have we learned nothing from that history?

CHAPTER 4

Cloudy Crystal Ball: Predictive Policing

___

"Technology designed without the end user in mind, that does not take policy into account from the start, and that is developed from a pure technology focus will only create new problems."

— KATHLEEN M. CARLEY, DIRECTOR OF THE
CENTER FOR COMPUTATIONAL ANALYSIS OF
SOCIAL AND ORGANIZATIONAL SYSTEMS
AT CARNEGIE MELLON UNIVERSITY

In 2007, just five years after Bratton was named Chief of the LAPD, he invited researchers to experiment on the LAPD. Enter UCLA anthropology professor Jeffrey Brantingham. Brantingham bought into the notion after one crime is committed in an area, more are likely to follow—sound familiar? Brantingham's research team adapted a model that predicts earthquake aftershocks to try to forecast property theft. Brantingham said if he was given the LAPD's crime data, he would apply an algorithm that could produce five-hundred-square-foot boxes showing where property crimes would most likely occur (Moravec, 2019).

This program became PredPol, the most widely used predictive policing algorithm in the US. One year after the LAPD's collaboration with Brantingham, Los Angeles became the first city to experiment with predictive policing.

In PredPol's own words, predictive, or algorithmic, policing "uses computer models, supported by prior crime and environmental data, to anticipate risk of crime and inform actions to prevent crime." An Illinois Freedom of Information Act request filed by the Chicago-based Lucy Parsons Labs led to the release of a "Best Practices and Training Guide" for the PredPol predictive policing software (Brown, 2018). The now-public guide provides a great deal of insight into the tool's design and deployment philosophy. For instance, Pred-Pol fully embraces the problematic broken windows theory of policing.

4. Broken-windows policing 'in the box'...

Under broken-windows policing, misdemeanor crimes are seen as the gateway to more serious crimes. Problem solving 'in the box' that is oriented towards reducing misdemeanor crime may also reduce felony crime.

Based on images of its user interface, the PredPol tool looks a lot like Google Maps with a "surveillance state" add-on. Its trademark five-hundred-square-foot boxes are color-coded for different types of crimes. PredPol also encourages officers to "get in the box." Although over-policing has been shown to erode trust between law enforcement and their communities, particularly communities of color, PredPol takes the opposite approach, suggesting to use the software to seek out crime during officers' downtime.

The User Interface lets you quickly set options and generate prediction reports.

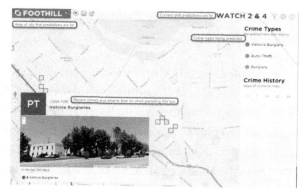

Around the same time Brantingham was developing PredPol, the LAPD contacted Craig Uchida, the president of the consulting firm Justice & Security Strategies. Uchida was also a former senior executive within the US Department of Justice, where he oversaw grants to develop predictive policing methods. He proposed a program that would use the LAPD's past crime data to find geographical areas of gun violence. The idea was such a program would help the department focus patrols where they would most likely be needed. After the LAPD acquired the necessary funding, the Los Angeles Strategic Extraction and Restoration Program—LASER for short, of course—was created.

The Los Angeles and Santa Cruz Police Departments were ahead of other cities in testing the predictive policing model, but other cities quickly followed suit. Soon, Palm Beach County, Florida; Memphis, Tennessee; Chicago, Illinois; Minneapolis, Minnesota; and Dallas, Texas, started testing their own predictive policing models. Federal seed money from the Department of Justice enabled other jurisdictions to test the technology as well (Ferguson, 2012). Predictive policing was becoming such a big deal in 2011, *Time* magazine called it one of the fifty best inventions of the year (Grossman et al., 2011).

In May 2013, a federal judge provisionally lifted the federal consent decree on the LAPD, ending federal oversight. Freed from a binding agreement with the Department of Justice that implemented major police reforms and frequent audits, this court order ushered in a new era for the LAPD. Uchida cowrote a paper for the Department of Justice that claimed LASER was "analogous to laser surgery, where a trained medical doctor uses modern technology to remove tumors or improve eyesight" (Uchida et al., 2012).

Both PredPol and LASER were funded by the federal Bureau of Justice Assistance (Ahmed, 2018). LASER was shut down in 2019 after the LAPD's inspector general released an internal audit that found significant problems with the program, including inconsistencies in how individuals were selected and kept in the system (Puente, 2019). In April 2020, the LAPD announced it would stop using PredPol but would seek out alternative predictive systems. Some other police departments have also discontinued their PredPol programs (Miller, 2020). In June 2020, Santa Cruz, one of the first cities in the US to adopt predictive policing, became the first in the country to ban the policy altogether (Ibarra, 2020).

But how do predictive policing models work?

These systems take inputs like locations, events, and historical crime rates to predict where and when crimes are more likely to happen. Police departments across the country use these predictive algorithms to identify hotspots and strategize about where to send their officers. PredPol, for example, breaks locations up into five-hundred-by-five-hundred-foot blocks and updates its predictions throughout the day, sort of like a crime weather forecast.

If it sounds too good to be true, it's because it is.

The problem of predictive algorithms lies with the data they rely on. As we have already seen, the history of policing in America has been far from fair or objective. How can we expect models built on that history to be fair or objective? According to the Office of Juvenile Justice Delinquency Prevention, an office of the Department of Justice, you are more than twice as likely to be arrested if you are Black than if you are white. A Black person is five times more likely to be stopped without just cause than a white person. If algorithms are replicating standard police practices, won't these same biases be reproduced?

By law, the algorithms cannot use race as a predictor; however, other variables like socioeconomic background, education, and zip code act as proxies for race. So even without considering race, these tools are racist.

University of Pennsylvania law professor Dorothy Roberts, an acclaimed scholar of race, gender, and the law, argues predictive policing in and of itself is problematic. "Racism has always been about predicting, about making certain racial groups seem as if they are predisposed to do bad things and therefore justify controlling them," she said during a July 2020 virtual panel (*Haymarket Books*, 2020).

According to a 2019 study commissioned by the UK government's Centre for Data Ethics and Innovation, designating certain areas as crime hotspots primes police officers to expect trouble when on patrol, making them more inclined to stop or arrest people in those areas based on prejudice rather than need.

Predictive policing systems also use dirty data, or data that contains erroneous or misrepresentative information. In jurisdictions across the country, predictive policing systems are built on data that was produced from racially biased, broken windows policing practices and policies. "The concern with dirty data is that it reflects the environment in which the data was created," said Rashida Richardson, lawyer and director of policy research at the AI Now Institute at NYU. "So, if it was created in a place where there is consistent discriminatory and unlawful police practices, that will be embedded in the data." (*The Berkman Klein Center for Internet & Society*, 2019). When this dirty data is used in predictive policing systems, those systems will likely reproduce the systemic biases baked into the data. In other words, we are taking bad data and using it to teach tools to produce bad results, creating a feed-forward loop.

Police departments are relying more and more on predictive algorithms. Two reasons are commonly cited: budget cuts and the misguided belief algorithms are more objective than humans.

Many police departments have turned to predictive policing systems as a cost-savings measure. As a result of budget cuts, police departments have been prioritizing efficiency. Yeshimabeit Milner, co-founder and director of Data for Black Lives, a grassroots collective of activists and computer scientists using data to reform the criminal justice system, says due to cities' budget constraints, police departments have been replacing police officers with algorithms (Heaven, 2020).

But what's so wrong with being efficient? After all, the promise of predictive policing algorithms and machine learning was to make more fair and more objective policing decisions. However, mounting evidence shows human biases have made their way into these algorithms because machine learning models are trained on biased police data. Instead of removing racism, these algorithms are simply better at hiding it. Many critics view these tools as a form of tech-washing, where a cloak of objective neutrality hides mechanisms that perpetuate inequities in society.

Esha Bhandari is the deputy director of the ACLU's Speech, Privacy, and Technology Project, where she focuses on the impact of big data and AI on civil liberties. When I spoke with her, she talked about the way AI design can shield government actors from accountability while encoding policy decisions. "To escape accountability, the government can point to a system and say, 'Well, the AI says this person should remain locked up' or 'The AI system says this person shouldn't get any benefits,' but it's actually just masking a policy choice for why this person should remain locked up or why that person shouldn't get benefits," Bhandari said. "We have to really interrogate what we're designing these systems to do and figure out what questions we're really asking them to answer. Absent a narrow set of mathematical or similar types of questions, AI is often asked to reify policy choices."

Because arrest data is frequently used to train predictive policing tools, and police are known to arrest more people in Black and other minority neighborhoods, this leads the algorithm to direct more policing to those areas, resulting in more arrests. So what if we used other data instead?

Instead of using police data, in 2021, Nil-Jana Akpinar and Alexandra Chouldechova at Carnegie Mellon University and Maria De-Arteaga at the University of Texas at Austin used crime reports from victims. This team of researchers built their own predictive algorithm using the same model found in popular tools like PredPol, then trained the model on victim reports.

When the team compared their tool's predictions against actual crime data, they found it made significant errors. For instance, in areas where few crimes were reported, the tool predicted about 20 percent of the actual hotspots, the locations with a high rate of crime. On the other hand, in areas with a high number of reported crimes, the tool predicted 20 percent more hotspots than there really were.

In other words, according to the team's findings, data from victim reports is also skewed. The problem with victim reports is Black people are more likely to be reported for a crime than white people. Richer white people are more likely to report a poorer Black person than the other way around. Black people are also more likely to report other Black people. As with arrest data, this reality results in Black neighborhoods being flagged as crime hotspots more often than they should (Heaven, 2020).

For Richardson, these results highlight how various systemic and social factors distort crime data. "Victim reporting is also related to community trust or distrust of police," Richardson told the *MIT Technology Review*. "So if you are in a community with a historically corrupt or notoriously racially biased police department, which will affect how and whether people report crime." In this case, a predictive tool may underestimate the level of crime in an area, so it will not get the policing it needs.

It seems there's no easy or obvious solution. Akpinar and Chouldechova tried to adjust their model to account for the biases they observed but lacked the data to make much of a difference, concluding "it is unclear if debiasing victim crime reporting data is any easier than the unsuccessful previous efforts of mitigating bias introduced by arrest data."

Still, despite academic research and even government investigations and reports finding significant issues with predictive policing programs, politicians and police officials remain undeterred. Worse yet, we know very little about predictive policing tools. If information is power, the powerful actively hide and hoard it. Information about what tools are used, how they are being used, and who is using them is extremely opaque.

Most tools are licensed to police departments by a variety of software companies, state authorities, and researchers. Some systems are proprietary; some are not. There is no uniformity or standard. Oftentimes, researchers will just take the tools' outputs and do their best to recreate the results.

The typical defense from companies that build and sell these tools is they cannot share information because it would give away trade secrets or proprietary information. As a result, very few predictive policing tools have actually been studied in any meaningful way and even though some information is out there, the vast majority of it is only known by a handful of people. There is no way to see if these systems actually work.

For instance, in 2012, when New Orleans' murder rate was the sixth-highest in the United States, the New Orleans Police Department partnered with Palantir Technologies, a secret data-mining company with seed money from the Central Intelligence Agency's (CIA) venture capital firm, In-Q-Tel. Palantir provided software to a secretive predictive policing program that traced people's ties to gang members, outlined criminal histories, analyzed social media, and predicted the likelihood individuals would commit violence or become a victim. The partnership between NOPD and Palantir was extended three times and expired in February 2018, and the public didn't know about this until an investigation by *The Verge* was published that same month (Winston, 2018).

New Orleans' political and community leaders—including city council members—were not told about the NOPD-Palantir partnership. The program escaped public notice and scrutiny because Palantir presented the partnership as a "philanthropic relationship" with the city through former mayor Mitch Landrieu. The agreement between Palantir and New Orleans never went through a public procurement process; never received city council sign-off; and never underwent any sort of public debate or commenting process (Winston, 2018).

For my *Lord of the Rings* fans out there, you may know a palantír, also known as a seeing stone, as a magical artifact used to see virtually any part of the world in J.R.R. Tolkien's Middle-earth. A palantír is essentially a magic mass surveillance tool. Life really does imitate art.

If you don't know much about Palantir, that's by design. The company was founded in May 2003 but did not go public on the New York Stock Exchange until September 2020. Palantir largely focuses on data gathering and analysis. With about 1.5 billion dollars in federal government contracts alone, Palantir is mostly providing its services to government agencies, such as the Department of Defense, the Department of Justice, and Homeland Security, including ICE (Fried, 2019).

* * *

Liz O'Sullivan is the CEO of a new algorithmic fairness company, first incorporated by Dr. Rumman Chowdhury, called Parity and previously was a cofounder of Arthur, an AI model monitoring company. She has spent ten years in tech, mainly in the AI space, and dedicated her career to making the world safer and less discriminatory by limiting the use of AI while installing safety constraints to protect those most at risk from AI harm. She also advocates with the Campaign to Stop Killer Robots at the United Nations.

In March 2017, O'Sullivan, alongside a coalition of activist groups, worked closely with S.T.O.P. founder Albert Fox Cahn to introduce the Public Oversight of Surveillance Technology (POST) Act. The purpose of the bill was to increase transparency over the NYPD's use of new surveillance technologies by requiring the NYPD to disclose basic information about the tools it uses and the safeguards in place to protect the privacy and civil liberties of New Yorkers. It was unpopular with the NYPD and the coalition had trouble getting a majority support from the city council.

Finally, in June 2020, the POST Act passed. "Only in the wake of the Black Lives Matter protests and all the surveillance that the police were deploying on those organizers, including some drone surveillance, were we able to finally pressure the city council enough to move forward with the POST Act," O'Sullivan explained during our interview.

In February 2021, I worked with Han from law firm Eisenberg & Baum to organize and host public forums to share information with the local community and discuss concerns about the NYPD's surveillance capabilities. We also drafted and submitted a public comment calling for greater transparency with respect to NYPD datasets and third-party vendors. Although we assumed the police deployed advanced tools to surveil New York City, we still found ourselves surprised by the POST Act disclosures.

"When we were putting together the forum, I was very concerned about these premature technologies that still have serious deficiencies—not just technological deficiencies, but also a lack of policies built around its use and privacy protections," Han said while we reflected on the public forum we organized. "I was worried about how our government was able to use such premature technologies to surveil many aspects of our lives in such ways I never even imagined was happening until the POST Act disclosures were made."

In February 2020, the AI Now Institute's executive director, Andrea Nill Sánchez, testified before the European Parliament LIBE Committee Public Hearing on "Artificial Intelligence in Criminal Law and Its Use by the Police and Judicial Authorities in Criminal Matters." Her message was simple: "predictive policing systems will never be safe or just until the criminal justice system they're built on is reformed."

Predictive policing is riddled with ethical problems and a lack of transparency. This challenge, however, is not just a technical one. This technology carries with it the heavy weight of what policing has done to marginalized and vulnerable groups, especially Black people and poor people. We need to come to terms with our history and the systemic biases that infect these tools. Before we start rewriting code and reassessing what variables these algorithms are taking in, a more fundamental question must be answered: should machines even be deciding how policing works in America?

CHAPTER 5

Smile! You're on Camera: Video Surveillance

———

"In the twenty-first century, there are cameras everywhere—except where our food comes from, where our energy comes from, and where our waste goes."

— ZIYA TONG, AUTHOR OF *THE REALITY BUBBLE*

For years, we have known webcams are fairly easy to hack and it is generally good practice to cover up that webcam with at least a sticky note. One of my favorite social media phenomena—and yes, it is a phenomenon—to come out of this public awareness is the so-called "FBI agent" meme. Since late 2017, netizens have seemingly come to terms with the realities of mass surveillance with jokes about their assigned FBI agent reading messages and watching them react to online content, such as videos or songs. First popularized on Twitter, the tweets are often brief stories involving the narrator doing something in private only to remember someone is in fact watching through their webcam. In many variations of this meme, the government agent assumes a nurturing role, offering support, sending advice via iMessage, or inquiring about the mental health of the narrator. The agent in many of these wholesome tweets wants the best for the subject they are assigned to surveil.

But truth is stranger than fiction (and memes). You are constantly being watched. There's just no need to hijack the camera on your phone or laptop when the cameras are already everywhere around you.

First announced in 2014, China's controversial social credit system uses a combination of big data and facial recognition technology to monitor citizens and score them based on their deeds. According to data from the People's Bank of China, the nation's central bank, the social credit system already covered 1.02 billion people by the end of 2019 (Lee, 2020). Millions of people in China have social scores low enough to be labelled as untrustworthy on an official blacklist. The social score can determine what rights are available to people. Blacklisted individuals, for instance, may be prevented from buying plane or train tickets and barred from working as civil servants or in certain industries (He, 2019).

To no one's surprise, China's social credit system has been given widespread negative reception by the media in the West. The system has been described as a "digital dictatorship" and a "real-life *Black Mirror* nightmare" (Carney, 2020; Palin, 2018). Aside from Western coverage lacking the more nuanced perception from within China, with many ordinary

Chinese people welcoming the social credit system, the criticisms directed at China are also lacking serious reflection on similarities with the US (Wang, 2019).

This idea of a social credit system is not unique to China. For quite some time now, we have all been scored in one way or another. In the US, data brokers like Experian, Equifax, and FICO score us based on whether we pay our debts on time. This score is used by lenders and mortgage providers. Uber drivers and passengers rate each other too. If your score is too low, you're kicked off of the platform, or at least have a much tougher time using it.

"We are all grappling, every day, with algorithmic determinism. Somebody's algorithm somewhere has assigned you a score, and as a result, you are paying more or less money for toilet paper when you shop online. You are being shown better or worse mortgages. You are more or less likely to be profiled as a criminal," said Amy Webb, futurist, author, and founder of the Future Today Institute, in *Coded Bias*, the must-watch documentary on algorithmic bias. "The key difference between the United States and in China is that China's transparent about it" (Kantayya, 2020).

We can all agree the mass public surveillance in China is astounding and terrifying, but we may be more hesitant to draw a one-to-one comparison with the US's surveillance of its own citizens. Data compiled by IHS Markit, reported by *The Wall Street Journal*, shows a one-to-one comparison is actually pretty accurate (Lin and Purnell, 2019).

While China in 2018 had one camera for every 4.1 people, the US had one camera for every 4.6 people in the same year. You read that right: the US, like China, has about one surveillance camera for every four people. China's camera count is expected to rise to over 560 million by 2021, representing the largest share of surveillance devices installed globally, with the US rising to around eighty-five million cameras. According to IHS Markit, one billion surveillance cameras will be installed globally by the end of 2021.

"During the past few years, coverage of the surveillance market has focused heavily on China's massive deployments of cameras and artificial intelligence technology," said IHS Markit analyst Oliver Philippou. "What's received far less attention is the high level of penetration of surveillance cameras in the United States. With the US nearly on par with China in terms of camera penetration, future debate over mass surveillance is likely to concern America as much as China" (Lin and Purnell, 2019).

Without drawing much attention or fanfare, cameras have quickly cropped up in cities, towns, and neighborhoods across the US, removing any expectation of privacy you might have once you step out of your home.

"You modify your behavior when you know you're being watched," Brandon del Pozo told me when I asked him about the typical person's expectation of privacy. "You could be walking through Times Square and there could be thousands of people around you, but you don't necessarily feel like you're being watched. Now, with surveillance technology, we're routinely being watched in a very substantive way in public. That can put demands on our behavior that seem to invade our privacy as normal people—not as criminal suspects trying to evade capture, but just as people.

"In 2005, before surveillance cameras were all the rage in the US, the NYPD was looking to install more surveillance cameras," del Pozo said, reflecting on his time in the NYPD. "I told the chiefs it's like we're recreating this panopticon for New Yorkers. The panopticon was designed to efficiently control people's behavior in a prison. I don't want to make this city like that."

The panopticon is a building concept where a tower is placed at the center of a circle of prison cells. This system of control was designed by English philosopher and social theorist Jeremy Bentham in the eighteenth century. The idea behind this design is to allow prisoners to be observed by a single security guard with one key characteristic: at any given time, none of the inmates can tell if they are being watched.

Although it is impossible for a single guard to observe all of the inmates' cells at once, the mere fact the inmates cannot know when they are being watched means they are motivated to act as though they are being watched at all times. The inmates are effectively compelled to regulate their own behavior (The Ethics Centre, 2017).

The word "panopticon" is derived from the Greek word *panoptes*, which means "all-seeing."

But law enforcement doesn't have to do it alone. Sure, there are tens of millions of surveillance cameras at their disposal, but as technology develops, it also gets more affordable. When technology becomes more affordable, it also becomes more readily available to everyday people.

When I met with Brett Max Kaufman, senior staff attorney at the ACLU's Center for Democracy and adjunct professor at NYU School of Law's Technology Law and Policy Clinic, he talked me through a hypothetical about the government and bodegas. "A practical reality that gives me a lot of comfort is that even if every bodega in New York is recording the exterior streets, it's very cumbersome for the government to acquire every recording," Kaufman said. "For that reason, when there's a crime in the area, the police go to the bodega that may have a video of what happened. They either get it with a warrant or it's handed over voluntarily and they use it to solve the crime. They don't get six months of video; they just get that night or maybe just a few minutes when the crime was committed. It ends up being naturally limited."

But the affordability of security cameras is just one piece. Now, individual households can equip their homes with private surveillance systems and—thanks to the Internet of Things (devices that use the internet to exchange data with other devices)—these systems are connected to cloud-enabled repositories and can share data over the internet.

This technology invites law enforcement into your home.

Amazon's signature home security product, the Ring Video Doorbell, has played a key role in extending the reach of law enforcement into private property and expanding the government's ability to peer into our everyday lives. To top it all off, once a Ring user agrees to release video content to law enforcement, there is no way to revoke access. There are also virtually no limitations on how that content can be used and stored or who it can be shared with. One journalist has called Ring "the largest corporate-owned, civilian-installed surveillance network that the US has ever seen" (Bridges, 2021).

Market research firm Strategy Analytics estimates 16 percent of US households use video doorbells like Amazon's Ring or Google's Nest. That's over twenty million homes in the US with video doorbells. And get this: since Amazon bought Ring in 2018, it has brokered more than eighteen hundred partnerships with local law enforcement agencies, who can request recorded video content from Ring users without a warrant. In other words, in just three years, Ring connected about one in ten police departments across the US with the ability to access recorded content from millions of privately-owned home security cameras (Bridges, 2021).

"When a corporation is giving direct access to data through an agreement with law enforcement, that company has basically been deputized to be an arm of the police department," Kaufman said.

The fact Ring cameras are owned by private civilians is crucial. The Fourth Amendment was designed to limit police power and prevent privacy intrusions by the government (Tokson, 2020). As a result, the police cannot simply install cameras on, for example, utility poles across the street from your house. However, by requesting access to recordings, typically without a warrant, the police are given a backdoor into private video recordings of people in residential and public spaces that would otherwise be protected by the Fourth Amendment. Amazon's partnership with law enforcement across the country allows the police to completely sidestep the privacy protections afforded to us by the Constitution.

Ring effectively turns your neighbor's home security system into a personal FBI agent. Like the agent in those memes, these cameras are always watching.

Jay Stanley is a senior policy analyst with the ACLU's Speech, Privacy, and Technology Project, where he researches, writes, and speaks about technology-related privacy and civil liberties issues and their future. "Imagine that there was a police officer stationed every block in your neighborhood. It would feel really oppressive," Stanley said. "Yet we could have the equivalent level of oppression just by installing cameras that are practically invisible."

An analysis of data from Ring, Fatal Encounters, and Mapping Police Violence indicates, between 2015 and 2020, roughly half of the law enforcement agencies that partner with Ring have been responsible for at least one fatal encounter. In fact, those agencies have been responsible for over a third of fatal police encounters nationwide (Kelley, 2020).

Accessing private video recordings is just one way the government surveils us. Law enforcement agencies have plenty of public cameras at their disposal as well. Automated license plate readers (ALPRs), for example, are high-speed, computer-controlled camera systems that are usually attached to utility poles, streetlights, highway overpasses, or police cars. Like the name implies, these devices capture all license plate numbers that come into view, along with the location, date, and time. ALPRs often capture photographs of the vehicle, driver, and passengers as well. All of this data is uploaded to a central server that is accessible by law enforcement (Electronic Frontier Foundation, 2021).

I think most of us would agree license plates are a good thing. When you're driving a three-thousand-pound object that can kill people even when you're just distracted for a couple seconds, there needs to be a way to show this object is licensed, registered, and inspected. The government slaps this metal rectangle with numbers on the outside of your car and that all still seems fine. But the government starts buying up license plate data from private data brokers or photographing license plates and collecting location data for where that photograph was taken.

"It sounds so modest at first," del Pozo said. "But I find it really disturbing that the private sector is collecting millions of license plate reads and selling them to the government to use for enforcement."

And yet, in two of the homicides del Pozo was responsible for investigating during his time as police chief in Burlington, Vermont, ALPRs played an important role in identifying the suspects. In one of those cases, three people murdered a homeless person and all the police had was the license plate of the car that left town.

"We were able to eventually apprehend them in San Diego because as they got closer to the Mexican border, their license plate got picked up by the US Border Patrol license plate readers. That's how we found them," del Pozo said. "Maybe we would have found them later, but we had no idea where they were. The license plate readers helped us catch these murderers. You can see why I'm so equivocal about this. That was a genuine public safety benefit."

While apprehending murderers is a positive outcome, we also need to keep in mind how intrusive this level of surveillance and data collection can be for everyday civilians.

Sure, a one-off picture of your license plate on a busy highway may not seem like a big deal. However, data collected over time can paint an intimate portrait of a driver's life. The government can use ALPRs to target people who drive to immigration clinics, Planned Parenthood health centers, gun shops, union meetings, protests, or places of religious worship. ALPR vendors have stated police can use the collected information to find out where a license plate has been in the past, determine whether a vehicle was at a crime scene, identify travel patterns, and even discover vehicles that may be associated with each other.

"It's death by a thousand cuts," del Pozo said. We may not mind little bits of our information—an image of our license plate here, a video of us walking down the street there—but what if all that data was brought together? "Discussing this data individually seems modest, but when you combine them all, you get a very intimate portrait of peoples' lives. You end up knowing someone's life in a very, very intimate way."

Luckily, security cameras and ALPRs are generally stuck in just one location. But what if the cameras could follow you around? Developments in drone technology have transformed package delivery and military reconnaissance alike. Why not every-day policing?

Gone are the days of officers manually flying a drone from a computer or controller. Using technology that enables self-driving cars, today's drones are starting to navigate and avoid obstacles on their own. In 2018, the police department in Chula Vista, California, was the first in the US to use autonomous drones as first responders. There, drones are already integrated into the police response to emergencies. According to a 2020 *New York Times* article, "after an emergency call comes in, officers give the drone a location, and it flies to that point on its own—before returning on its own" (Metz, 2020).

In addition to video and photographs, drones can gather license plate information with mounted ALPRs, determine GPS locations, and even intercept cellphone calls.

As the watchers become more automated and advanced, perhaps we need to think about what police were able to do before this technology was developed. While the law allows police to follow you, watch you, and eventually use that information against you, deploying new technologies that are not readily available to the public presents new problems. Cameras and drones are not only able to watch someone for long periods of time, but they can send images, videos, and audio to police databases.

When we think of drones, we tend to think of small, unmanned aircrafts that hover in the sky, but police departments are also deploying ground drones, like the New York Police Department's Digidog. This four-legged surveillance drone became the center of privacy and public spending debates after the NYPD first started deploying it in October 2020. Digidog has been deployed as part of the NYPD's response to hostage situations and home invasions, but the public backlash seemed to reach a boiling point when police officers used Digidog at a public housing building in Manhattan in April 2021. Many people viewed this use as emblematic of how disproportionately aggressive law enforcement can be when policing poor communities (Zaveri, 2021).

Virginia Eubanks is a political science professor at the University at Albany, SUNY and author of *Automating Inequality*. "The future is already here—it's just not evenly distributed. And what they tend to mean when they say that is that rich people get the fancy tools first, and then it goes last to the poor," Eubanks said in *Coded Bias*. "But in fact, what I've found is the absolute reverse, which is the most punitive, most invasive, most surveillance-focused tools that we have, they go into poor and working communities first. And then, if they work, after being tested in this environment where there's low expectation that people's rights will be respected, then they get ported out to other communities" (Kantayya, 2020).

For example, government's use of surveillance technology frequently has a disproportionate impact on immigrant communities. "A lot of new systems and technologies are deployed on immigrants first. It's easy for the government to claim that it's doing something in the name of national security or border security," Esha Bhandari told me. It often doesn't stop there, though. "For people who may be inclined to think 'this doesn't affect me,' we've seen it over and over again: technologies that are used in a border context or against immigrant communities eventually get widespread deployment and affect everybody."

If government encroachment on your privacy is not enough to scare you, maybe the cost of some of this technology will. The NYPD signed a $94,200 contract for Boston Dynamics' Spot robot, roughly enough for a $74,500 robot dog and a 360-degree "Spot Cam" camera for $21,800 (Amadeo, 2021). Seeing taxpayer money spent on what is essentially an expensive toy without much of a use case is frustrating when agencies that provide helpful services and programs are facing budget cuts. After the NYPD deployed the Digidog in the Bronx in early 2021, US representative Alexandria Ocasio-Cortez (D-NY) argued the money should instead be invested in communities. She tweeted, "When was the last time you saw next-generation, world-class technology for education, healthcare, housing, and so on consistently prioritized for underserved communities like this?"

The Digidog sparked an immediate backlash, with critics noting police dogs have historically been used to suppress and intimidate communities of color. In April 2021, New York's mayor, Bill de Blasio, ordered the seventy-pound robot dog to be returned to Boston Dynamics. De Blasio said he was "glad the Digidog was put down" and a city government spokesperson added, "It's creepy, alienating, and sends the wrong message to New Yorkers" (Helmore, 2021).

Privacy advocates like Stanley are worried about how the ever-increasing number of cameras coupled with autonomous surveillance will be used to target marginalized communities or unfairly enforce laws that conflict with today's norms. "The way the government has used this technology is pretty intrusive and can become extremely chilling," Stanley said. For example, drones could easily be used to identify people and restrict activity during protests.

Stanley believes while there are very good arguments for banning government use of facial recognition, the same outright ban of camera surveillance and video analytics is going to be much more difficult. "It's just going to be too useful in too many ways. It's going to be more like trench warfare, where we try to stop the bad applications and try to get more transparency," Stanley told me.

Cameras have been used in many beneficial ways, from spotting distracted driving on highways to detecting when someone in a crowded swimming pool may be drowning and alerting the lifeguards on duty. "Oftentimes, the technology starts with the most sympathetic use cases where nobody can really object to it," Stanley said. "But then that power and scope expand, raising serious privacy problems."

These cameras are flagging distracted driving on highways, spotting suspicious activity in airports, and recording strangers knocking on your front door. That all seems innocuous. It might even make us feel safer, knowing we have something or someone watching.

But these cameras are watching all the time—and they're everywhere.

"Our intuitions have traditionally had a very well-defined sense of what a public space is and we distinguish between the expectation of privacy in public and in private. Surveillance technology is turning that intuition on its head," del Pozo said. "The idea that public space is a space in which we have no expectation of privacy—is that an anachronistic concept? Does that basic intuition no longer hold up now that even the slightest semblance of privacy no longer exists in so many public spaces? It's not enough to point to case law to set our expectations of privacy in public, because it's all case law that was decided before an era of omni-surveillance."

The law is clear: your face is open to the public, so you have zero expectation of privacy.

Let's say a police officer is standing on a street corner and you're just walking by. Your face is exposed, so that officer can clearly see it. Fine, that makes sense.

Now, let's replace that officer with a camera. Chances are you have no idea it's even there. Its watchful eye is inescapable and unavoidable. You're just walking down the street and suddenly your face has been captured by a device that has significantly more space in its "brain" to store your face *and* a significantly better memory than any police officer. When your faceprint is captured and stored, there's probably no investigation taking place. So the collection of your faceprint is just a simple, inconspicuous administrative process. Yet taking an image of your face, converting it into a faceprint, and storing it serves only one purpose: to find something later.

Enter facial recognition.

CHAPTER 6

AI Spy with My Little Eye: Facial Recognition

———

"Writing and talk do not prove me, I carry the plenum of proof and every thing else in my face..."

— WALT WHITMAN, *SONG OF MYSELF*

In 2010, Facebook began using facial recognition in the US when it automatically tagged people in photos using its tag suggestions tool. The tool scanned a user's face and offered suggestions about who that person was.

At that time, my younger brother and I used to laugh at how the social media platform would get us confused in photos. When we uploaded photos of ourselves, Facebook's suggested photo tags would often mistake us for each other. Full disclosure: my brother and I are not twins. Even back then, I just figured Facebook's algorithm was no good at differentiating East Asian faces.

A couple of years before Facebook rolled out this tag suggestions feature, Illinois adopted the Biometric Information Privacy Act, otherwise known as BIPA. It remains one of the most protective biometric data and privacy laws in the US, requiring any entity that collects biometric data—such as fingerprints, voice prints, retinal or iris scans, and faceprints—to get informed consent from those individuals whose data it collects. Those entities are also required to protect the biometric data they store in the same way they would other sensitive, personally identifiable information, like e-mail addresses and passwords (Illinois General Assembly, 2021).

Of course, Facebook never went through the trouble of getting that express consent from users in Illinois. So in 2020, after a five-year lawsuit, Facebook paid 650 million dollars to a class of users in Illinois that argued Facebook's facial recognition tool was in violation of BIPA (Cox, 2021).

Still, for my brother and I, correcting Facebook's suggested photo tags was at most an inconvenience. We laughed about the faulty facial recognition tool at the time because it was funny, but it was also harmless.

The same cannot be said for Robert Julian-Borchak Williams.

Williams is a forty-three-year-old man who lives with his wife of eleven years and two young daughters in their home in Farmington Hills, a quiet suburb twenty-five miles northwest of Detroit. Williams is a logistics planner and has been working at an automotive supply company for eight years. When he isn't working, he enjoys playing with his daughters, grilling food for his family and neighbors, and playing basketball.

On October 2, 2018, a thief stole an estimated thirty-eight hundred dollars' worth of merchandise from a Shinola retail store in Detroit. Investigators got a hold of a security video that recorded the theft. Although the surveillance footage was poorly lit and the shoplifter never looked directly into the camera, a Detroit Police Department detective zoomed in on the grainy footage and ran it through facial recognition software.

On January 9, 2020, Williams was in his office at work when he received a call from the Detroit Police Department. They told him to come to the station to be arrested. Williams thought it had to be a prank.

An hour later, when Williams pulled into his driveway, a police car pulled up behind him, blocking him in. Two officers got out and handcuffed Williams on his front lawn, in front of his wife and two daughters, who were ages two and five at the time. They cried as they watched their father be placed in the police car.

The police wouldn't say why Williams was being arrested, only showing him a piece of paper with his photo, as well as the words "felony warrant" and "larceny."

Williams was taken to a detention center where he had his mugshot photographed, fingerprints and DNA taken, and was held overnight. Around noon the next day, two detectives took him to an interrogation room. When one of the detectives asked Williams when the last time he went to a Shinola store was, Williams said his wife and him had checked it out in 2014 to find a present for his brother-in-law's birthday. The detectives presented Williams with a still image of the surveillance footage they had collected from the Shinola store.

"Is this you?" asked the detective.

"Does this look like me? I hope you do not think all Black people look alike."

While Williams knew he did not commit the crime in question, he could not have known, as he sat in the Detroit interrogation room, that his case was likely the first known account of an American being wrongfully arrested based on a facial recognition algorithm's incorrect match.

On April 13, 2021, attorneys representing Williams filed a federal lawsuit against the city of Detroit; its police chief, James Craig; and Detroit police detective Donald Bussa for "the grave harm caused by the misuse of, and reliance upon, facial recognition technology."

Of course, the police have been using—and misusing—facial recognition technology long before Williams's encounter with it.

* * *

One of facial recognition's first appearances on the US public stage was at Super Bowl XXXV in 2001, where law enforcement officials used the technology on crowds at the event, scanning faces and comparing them to criminal mugshots (McCullagh, 2001). That year also saw the first widespread police use of facial recognition with a database operated by the Pinellas County Sheriff's Office, now one of the largest local databases in the country (Valentina-DeVries, 2020).

In 2011, facial recognition was used to confirm the identity of Osama bin Laden (Reuters Staff, 2011). Edward Snowden released documents from 2011 revealing the extent to which the US government was collecting images to build a federal facial recognition database. President Donald Trump in 2017 issued an executive order expediting the use of facial recognition at US borders and ports of entry, including airports (Alba, 2019).

Over the course of two decades, facial recognition technology went from a novelty to an everyday staple. Thanks to improvements in computing power and developments in machine learning, namely neural networks, facial recognition became a standard feature.

The Center on Privacy and Technology at Georgetown Law studied the widespread use of facial recognition, particularly in the law enforcement context. In 2016, they published a report titled "The Perpetual Line-Up." What was the key takeaway? One in two American adults is in a facial recognition database network that can be searched by police departments without a warrant (Garvie, Bedoya, and Frankle, 2016). Back then, law enforcement facial recognition already affected 117 million American adults. This technology was also unregulated and, even to this day, many have not been tested for accuracy on different groups of people. What happened to Williams in 2020 already tells us how misidentification can subject innocent people to police scrutiny and erroneous criminal charges.

Since this report, the facial recognition market has only gotten bigger and perhaps even more opaque. Clare Garvie is one of the authors of "The Perpetual Line-Up." She is a senior associate with the Center on Privacy & Technology at Georgetown Law whose research focuses on the use of facial recognition-derived evidence in criminal cases and the ways activists, public defenders, and policymakers can ensure the technology is under control.

Garvie found right around the time the report was published, many cities and police departments were interested in piloting different face surveillance programs. Parallel to the growing interest in its surveillance capabilities, facial recognition was also being used more and more as an investigative tool. When I asked Garvie about how law enforcement's use of facial recognition technology has changed since the 2016 report, she said she noticed a new trend.

"Because of widespread public pressure, particularly condemning face surveillance, many face surveillance programs have pretty much disappeared from public agencies," Garvie said. "I think law enforcement agencies would rather drop the novel biometric surveillance system in favor of retaining the investigative system."

"Investigative" may not have the same Orwellian ring to it as "surveillance," but there's still plenty to be worried about. The infamous Clearview AI has been making headlines the last few years for developing a facial recognition app that goes further than anything ever built by the US government or Silicon Valley tech giants. Clearview's system relies on a database of more than *three billion* images scraped from Facebook, YouTube, Venmo, and millions of other websites. Users upload a picture of someone and the app returns public photos of that person as well as links to where those photos appeared, typically social media profiles (Hill, 2020).

Clearview has been selling this app to law enforcement agencies at the state and federal level, including the FBI and Department of Homeland Security (Hill, 2020).

* * *

But how does facial recognition even work? What *is* facial recognition?

First and foremost, facial recognition is a type of biometric identification. Biometrics are unique markers that either identify or verify someone's identity using their intrinsic physical or behavior qualities. Fingerprints, for example, are probably the most well-known biometric, and law enforcement agencies have regularly used fingerprints to identify people for well over a century. Other biometrics that are becoming more common include DNA, iris scans, voiceprints, gait, and, of course, facial recognition.

Facial recognition algorithms extract identifying features from the face. These peaks and valleys that make up human facial features are called "nodal points." The algorithm identifies and measures them to determine an individual's identifying characteristics, such as distance between the eyes, width of the nose, shape of cheekbones, and length of the jawline.

Many facial recognition systems define which features are the best indicators of similarity through machine learning. During this learning process, an algorithm designed for facial recognition is fed pairs of face images of the same person. By repeatedly comparing different faces, the algorithm learns to pay more attention to the features that were the most reliable signals that the two images contained the same person.

The diversity of faces used to train an algorithm can influence the kinds of photos and faces an algorithm is most adept at examining. If the set of face images is skewed toward a certain race, the algorithm may be better at identifying members of that group compared to individuals of other groups (Garvie, Bedoya, and Frankle, 2016).

Facial recognition systems are generally designed to perform one of three tasks. The first type of system may be designed to identify an unknown person. For instance, a police officer would use this system to identify an unknown person in surveillance camera footage. Second, a facial recognition system can be designed to verify the identity of a known person. Smartphones use this type of system so users can rely on facial recognition to unlock their phones. The third type of facial recognition system is set up to look for specific, previously identified faces. These types of systems may be used to recognize wanted persons on a crowded street or subway platform (Lynch, 2020).

Facial recognition and other surveillance tools have been getting a lot of buzz lately, but state and local police began using facial recognition technology in the early 2000s. While the early systems were notoriously unreliable, today's law enforcement agencies have either acquired or are actively considering more sophisticated surveillance camera systems.

Some surveillance camera systems can capture the faces of passersby and identify them in real time. Police officers can also submit images of people's faces, taken in the field or lifted from photos or videos, and instantaneously compare them to photos in government databases, including mug-shots, jail booking records, and driver's licenses.

With the click of a button, today's police departments can identify a suspect caught committing a crime on camera, verify a driver's identity when they do not produce a license, or search for suspected fugitives in a state driver's license database (Schuppe, 2016).

The Pinellas County Sheriff's Office's facial recognition pro-gram is known as Face Analysis Comparison & Examination System (FACES) and it searches over thirty-three million faces, including twenty-two million Florida driver's license and ID photos and over eleven million law enforcement pho-tos. Florida's database is searched eight thousand times per month and the Florida police do not need reasonable sus-picion to run a search (Garvie, Bedoya, and Frankle, 2016).

Unlike DNA evidence, which is costly and can take a laboratory days to produce, facial recognition is inexpensive and convenient once a system is installed. This lower barrier to entry enables the police to incorporate the technology into their day-to-day work. Instead of reserving it for serious or high-profile cases, officers are using facial recognition to solve routine crimes and quickly identify people perceived to be suspicious.

The FBI quietly developed a massive facial recognition system which became fully operational in April 2015. A US Government Accountability Office report (GAO-19-579T) published in June 2019 indicates the FBI can draw from over 641 million photos in its facial recognition database. The FBI regularly uses facial recognition systems to identify individuals during the course of their investigations (Hirose, 2017).

As of July 2019, twenty-one states allow federal agencies, like the FBI, to run searches of driver's license and identification photo databases (Germain, 2019). In February 2020, the Department of Homeland Security said more than 43.7 million people in the US have been scanned by facial recognition technology, primarily to check the identity of people boarding flights and cruises and crossing borders (US Government Publishing Office, 2020).

Market research firm Grand View Research published a report in May 2021 that predicts the market for facial recognition technology will grow at an annual rate of 14.5 percent between 2020 and 2027, driven by "rising adoption of the technology by the law enforcement sector." In spite of its rapid adoption over the past two decades, facial recognition systems used by police are not required to undergo public or independent testing to determine accuracy or check for bias before being deployed on everyday citizens. Worse yet, when vendors do agree to have their products tested by government agencies like the National Institute of Standards and Technology, many products used by police are found to have a pattern of racial bias (Garvie and Frankle, 2016).

"If you look at the top three companies [in the field], none of them perform with 100 percent accuracy. So we're experimenting in real time with real humans," said Rashida Richardson, director of policy research at the AI Now Institute (Ivanova, 2020). Amazon's face-ID system, Rekognition, once identified Oprah Winfrey as male, while Microsoft's facial recognition system made the same error with Michelle Obama (Buolamwini, 2019). Rekognition also incorrectly matched twenty-eight members of Congress with people who have been arrested for a crime (Snow, 2018).

Looking at instances in which an algorithm wrongly identified two different people as the same person, a 2019 study published by NIST found that for facial recognition systems developed in the US, error rates were highest in West and East African and East Asian people and lowest in Eastern European individuals.

Repeating this exercise across a US mugshot database, NIST researchers found algorithms had the highest error rates for Indigenous people as well as high rates for Asian and Black women (Grother, Ngan, and Hanaoka, 2019). Given how often facial recognition systems get it wrong, this technology can entrench and enhance systemic bias in policing.

Bias in facial recognition is especially disturbing given policing practices, such as stop-and-frisk and the "war on drugs," have historically and systematically harmed poor communities of color, particularly Black communities.

In the US, Black people are more than twice as likely to be arrested than any other race and, by some estimates, up to two-and-a-half times more likely to be targeted by police surveillance. Not only are Black people more likely to be misidentified by facial recognition systems used by police, but they are also more likely to be enrolled in those systems and be subject to their processing. This overrepresentation in both mugshot databases and surveillance photos results in algorithms that consistently perform worse on Black people than on white people (Garvie and Frankle, 2016).

Even if false-positive match rates improve, "unfair use of facial recognition technology cannot be fixed with a software patch" (Buolamwini, 2018). Accurate facial recognition can still be used in disturbing and nefarious ways. For instance, the Baltimore Police Department used facial recognition to identify and arrest people who attended the 2015 protests against police misconduct following Freddie Gray's death (Powers, 2017). Additionally, ICE is interested in driver's license databases because several states issue driver's licenses to residents regardless of their immigration status (Germain, 2019).

For example, in Maryland, a state that grants special driver's licenses to undocumented immigrants, ICE has used facial recognition software to scan millions of Maryland driver's license photos without a warrant or any other form of state or court approval (Harwell and Cox, 2020). "These states have never told undocumented people that when they apply for a driver's license, they are also turning over their face to ICE," said Harrison Rudolph from Georgetown Law's Center on Privacy and Technology. "That is a huge bait-and-switch" (Edmondson, 2019).

* * *

While I believe the surveillance concerns of facial recognition will be ever-present, its prevalence in law enforcement investigation and identification is a very real risk to the public. The way facial recognition is applied in the investigative realm differs from the surveillance features that get more attention. "I tend to characterize a face recognition search from start to finish as a five-step process," Garvie said during our interview. "Only one of which is done by an algorithm."

First, the police obtain an image of someone's face. This image may be from security footage or police departments' "gang databases," which generally have poorly-defined inclusion criteria and a history of racial bias. NYPD officials have even acknowledged that as many as 95 percent of the people in its gang database are Black or Latinx (Coltin, 2018).

Here, determinations about image quality and the position of the face are made by a human analyst. Standards for how clear a face image should be, how obstructed the face is, or the angle of how the image is captured are rarely defined. Police departments have even relied on forensic sketches instead of photos, and in some cases, the police have even used photos of celebrities when they didn't have a photo of the actual suspect. For example, the NYPD famously fed its facial recognition system an image of actor Woody Harrelson when pixelated surveillance footage failed to produce a match (Emerson, 2019).

Second, the face image may get edited—in Photoshop. "There's a heavy reliance on Photoshop to bolster the performance of the algorithm, which is baffling from a forensic evidentiary perspective," said Garvie. "We've found Photoshop referenced in both police department policies and even job postings, which will request Photoshop proficiency as part of an analyst's qualifications. Not forensic face identification training, but Photoshop training."

The third step is where the algorithm is actually introduced. The algorithm takes in the image and examines pairs of faces. Most algorithms will either issue a numerical score reflecting the similarity of features or produce a list of possible matches. In other words, facial recognition is inherently probabilistic (Garvie, Bedoya, and Frankle, 2016). The algorithm does not produce binary "yes" or "no" answers. Instead, it identifies "more likely" or "less likely" matches.

Next, an analyst looks through the algorithm's output to decide whether there is a match. "This is a human relying on their ability to look at unfamiliar faces to determine whether or not someone's a match," Garvie said. "The US does not have certification requirements, and while some agencies may require training, a lot of them don't. Because there is no standard or regulation, the training being conducted is all over the map."

Finally, there's the investigative follow-up. This is where the police decide how to use this potential match. "Historically, in the US, a match is only considered an investigative lead. A match is not probable cause to make an arrest. Officers have to corroborate the lead in some way, shape, or form," Garvie explained. "Further corroboration is often not done or, when it is done, it's not done in a permissible way."

That's what happened when Williams was misidentified by the Detroit police. During the investigative follow-up in that case, detective Bussa tried to get a witness of the Shinola theft to identify Williams from a photo array. However, no one from the retail store wanted to appear in court or take part in the investigation.

That's when Bussa arranged to conduct a photo identification with Katherine Johnston, who worked for a business contracted by Shinola for loss prevention services. The problem was Johnston was not an eyewitness. She was not in the store at the time of the theft and had never seen Williams or the alleged shoplifter in person. Johnston's only association to this investigation was she watched the low-quality surveillance footage Bussa presented to her (Williams v. City of Detroit et al., 2021).

Failure to properly conduct an investigative follow-up and adequately corroborate the "match" ultimately resulted in Williams being misidentified and wrongfully arrested.

"All these human steps are very subjective, introduce the possibility of error, and are not controlled," Garvie said. "So the algorithm is just one piece. It doesn't matter how good the algorithm gets if the human in the loop is bad at their job."

When Joy Buolamwini was a college student using AI-powered facial detection software for a coding project, the robot she programmed couldn't detect her face. She had to borrow her white roommate's face to finish the assignment. When Buolamwini went on to work on another project as a graduate student at the MIT Media Lab, the AI system couldn't identify her face—until she wore a white mask (Buolamwini, 2018).

Buolamwini is one of the leading activists challenging algorithmic bias in decision-making systems. She founded the Algorithmic Justice League in 2016 and the research paper she wrote alongside Timnit Gebru, titled "Gender Shades," is considered one of the most important critiques of the race and gender bias found in some of the most widely used facial recognition systems in the world.

"AI systems are shaped by the priorities and prejudices—conscious and unconscious—of the people who design them," Buolamwini wrote in a 2018 *New York Times* article. She calls this phenomenon "the coded gaze."

A 2010 study conducted by NIST found "East Asian algorithms" developed in countries like China, South Korea, and Japan recognized East Asian facial features more accurately than Caucasian features. In contrast, "Western algorithms" designed in countries like France, Germany, and the US were substantially better at recognizing Caucasian faces. These results show the conditions in which an algorithm is developed, specifically the racial composition of its design team and training data set, can impact the accuracy of its results (Phillips et al., 2010).

Given facial recognition's well-documented tendency to mimic gender and racial biases, public institutions should be particularly mindful of how these systems are designed and applied to ensure they are not reinforcing biases that inform racist policing practices. But the regulatory landscape is inconsistent at best.

"In terms of regulation, it's been a bit of a binary. We've seen either nonaction or bans and moratoria. We're mainly seeing these regulations at the state and local level," Garvie noted during our interview. "There isn't agreement within the advocacy community around what appropriate regulation looks like, so I would characterize the regulatory approach as being incredibly patchwork and hyperlocal."

Facial recognition has and will continue to have a disparate impact on poor communities of color who are already subject to inequitable policing practices. At its core, police use of facial recognition is a question about the legitimacy of policing practices and how policing in the US must change (Najibi, 2020).

The police are not neutrally enforcing a body of law that automatically benefits everyone. Similarly, the tools the police wield are not deployed in fair and equitable ways. Until actionable steps are taken to interrogate the purpose and function of law enforcement in the US, calls for equitable facial recognition will remain entangled with calls to defund the police.

PART 3:

FALSE POSITIVE

CHAPTER 7

Smoking Gun or Smoke and Mirrors: Forensic Evidence

———

"When you've licked a stamp on your tax return, you've sent the government a DNA sample."

— VICTOR W. WEEDN, FORMER HEAD OF ARMED
FORCES DNA IDENTIFICATION LABORATORY

In January 2016, I started an internship at the Legal Aid Society in New York City. More specifically, I interned for the Criminal Defense Practice's DNA Unit, which at the time was not even three years old. The purpose of this unit is to assist in litigating cases involving DNA and forensic evidence. I was interested in exploring the ways DNA evidence was used in criminal cases, particularly because I had read about how DNA evidence was used to exonerate wrongly convicted people. However, a different story revealed itself the more

I studied the ways our criminal justice system used DNA evidence and DNA analysis algorithms.

My internship was only supposed to last until May 2016, but I ended up staying until May 2017. The formative experience not only crystallized my decision to attend law school but introduced me to the world of tech-washing and how injustice can hide in plain sight when it appears to be scientific or objective.

Since the early 2000s, the DNA laboratory at New York City's chief medical examiner made a name for itself as a forerunner in analyzing some of the most complex crime scene evidence. The lab introduced two techniques that allowed it to do something not even the FBI or other public labs were able to do: identify suspects from tiny DNA samples or samples that contained a mix of multiple peoples' genetic material.

The first technique was the "high-sensitivity testing" of trace DNA amounts, which allowed the lab to identify someone's DNA when very little genetic material was collected from a crime scene. Trace DNA usually refers to either very limited or invisible biological samples, or amounts of DNA less than one hundred picograms—that's one *trillionth* of a gram (van Oorschot, Ballantyne, and Mitchell, 2010).

Then, in April 2011, the lab rolled out its second technique: the Forensic Statistical Tool, or FST. This in-house DNA analysis software calculated the likelihood of a suspect's DNA being present in a mixture of multiple peoples' genetic material.

The lab's reputation spread. With these incredible techniques, the lab processed DNA evidence supplied not only by the New York police, but by about fifty other jurisdictions, some as far away as Bozeman, Montana, and Floresville, Texas. Police departments across the country were paying the lab eleven hundred dollars per sample analyzed.

High-sensitivity testing and FST legitimized forensic science and revolutionized the way DNA evidence was used by prosecutors. According to the New York lab, high-sensitivity DNA testing was used to analyze evidence samples in 3,450 criminal cases between 2006 and 2017. Similarly, the lab used FST in 1,350 criminal cases from 2011 to 2017.

Thousands of criminals were put away and the streets of New York City were made safer thanks to the infallible powers of science and technology.

Sounds a bit too good to be true, right?

In reality, scientists scrutinized these DNA analysis methods and questioned their validity. In court testimony, a former lab official stated she was fired for criticizing one method. A former member of the New York State Commission on Forensic Science said he was wrong when he approved their use. The first expert witness permitted by a judge to examine FST source code concluded its accuracy "should be seriously questioned."

A coalition of defense attorneys asked the New York State inspector general's office—the designated watchdog for the state's crime labs—to launch an inquiry into the use of the

DNA analysis methods used in thousands of criminal cases. Although the inspector general had no jurisdiction over the court system, any finding of flaws with the DNA analysis could flood the courts with lawsuits. Prior convictions could be revisited if the flawed evidence could be shown to change the outcome of a case.

How could this technology—unchecked, unvalidated, and unknown to the public—be used to convict someone? How could something with the potential to have profound effects on the public be used without being scrutinized by the public? Why are there virtually no laws or rules governing the way technology affects people's freedoms?

How did we get here?

* * *

DNA is a code that programs how we will develop, grow, and function. Humans have DNA that is 99.9 percent identical. The remaining 0.1 percent makes us unique. The fact humans and chimpanzees have just a 1 percent difference in their genetic makeup puts into perspective how significant a small difference can be (Elster, 2017).

DNA was first used to solve a crime nearly forty years ago. Since, DNA has been celebrated for its potential to identify criminals. When it comes to criminal trials, physical evidence, especially DNA evidence, is frequently considered to be the most convincing and is widely accepted as reliable proof of an individual's innocence or guilt. The value of physical evidence has also been cemented in the public imagination by portrayals on popular TV shows.

To appreciate the current state of DNA forensics and DNA databases in the US, we need to start in the UK, where DNA analysis was used for the first time to catch a murderer.

Alec Jeffreys was a genetics professor at the University of Leicester in England. In 1984, he discovered the technique of genetic fingerprinting, which allowed him to distinguish one individual from another (Arnaud, 2017).

When fifteen-year-old Dawn Ashworth was raped and murdered in nearby Leicestershire in July 1986, Jeffreys had only tested his DNA pattern recognition technique in paternity and immigration cases. Suddenly, the police wanted him to help solve Ashworth's murder as well as a similar one that occurred in 1983. The police already identified a suspect, Richard Buckland, who even confessed to Ashworth's murder.

Jeffreys agreed to help, analyzing DNA samples from the 1983 and 1986 crime scenes, as well as Buckland's DNA. Jeffreys found matching DNA from both crime scenes, but the DNA samples didn't belong to Buckland.

In response to this revelation, the police turned to a genetic dragnet, collecting blood and saliva samples from more than four thousand men in the Leicestershire area between the ages of seventeen and thirty-four and having Jeffreys analyze the DNA samples. When DNA from Colin Pitchfork, who had been evading the DNA dragnet, was analyzed, it matched the crime scene samples. In September 1987, Pitchfork was arrested. He was convicted and sentenced to life in prison in January 1988.

The mass DNA dragnet employed during the Pitchfork investigation may have inspired mass screening programs in the US. By 1994, authorized by the DNA Identification Act, the FBI established the Combined DNA Index System (CODIS), which collected DNA and supported the analysis of DNA (Ahmed, 2019). CODIS allows local, state, and national searches of the DNA Index System. As of March 2021, CODIS contains more than fourteen million offender profiles, more than four million arrestee profiles, and more than one million forensic profiles.

It's difficult to overstate the support for DNA as a crime-solving mechanism. DNA is praised for its potential to control crime in a more targeted and accurate way. It's true DNA testing has revealed more alleged perpetrators of crime and CODIS standardized the field (Ahmed, 2019). However, DNA evidence isn't as foolproof as people think.

When forensic evidence is ambiguous, contextual information, such as knowledge of a confession, can influence how forensic scientists evaluate evidence. This distorted evaluation, known as contextual bias, may result in miscarriages of justice (Curley and Munro, 2019).

Researchers Itiel E. Dror and Greg Hampikian conducted a study in 2011 that compared DNA interpretations between lab technicians and forensic experts. They sent identical DNA mixtures to seventeen different experts to see if they would come to the same conclusion as the original forensic analysis.

The seventeen forensic scientists arrived at vastly different results.

In their study, Dror and Hampikian found what the forensic scientist knows about the investigation, such as prosecutors relying on the lab results to move forward, may impact the interpretation of a DNA sample. It wouldn't be a stretch to conclude there must be some real-life cases of lab technicians or forensic experts making mistakes or stating there was a DNA match when there wasn't one (Shaer, 2016).

Clinton Hughes, a forensic DNA attorney at the Brooklyn Defender Services, argues this increasing reliance on DNA analysis software, coupled with pressures to produce results for prosecutors and police departments, can push labs to cut corners.

"Rather than manually looking at the forensic evidence and trying to come to their own conclusions, lab technicians are just relying on this software that dumbs it down for you," Hughes said in our interview. "There's pressure for crime labs to increase production and process more forensic evidence. Now, instead of using the software to check for mistakes or validate a lab technician's work, labs assume the technology is right the first time around. Labs rely less and less on expertise and training, so they also become less critical of the data the software spits out."

Worse yet, forensic science as a discipline has never been subjected to any rigorous scientific review. Instead, forensic evidence achieved "ubiquitous celebrity status" while remaining "shrouded in a cloak of infallibility and certainty in the public's imagination" (Cino, 2016).

This problem is further compounded by how evidence is presented in court. For instance, an expert witness may declare two fingerprints are a match, but that is—at most—just an informed opinion.

Fingerprints are generally compared by examining points of comparison. It may be true no two fingerprints are alike, but there is also no standard or agreement on just how many points of comparison are needed to prove it. In fact, the minimum number of points needed to declare two samples are a match *varies by jurisdiction* (MacDonald, 2019). With fingerprints, there is no way to quantify just how likely a match really is.

Furthermore, recent research reveals an unsettling and uncomfortable reality: forensic analysis can be subjective and fallible. For example, forensic evidence can occasionally be ambiguous due to factors like the presence of DNA on samples that come from more than one person (Dror, Charlton, and Péron, 2006). It is also possible for any of us to have DNA present at a crime scene—even if we were never there. DNA recovered at a crime scene could have wound up there at a time other than when the crime took place. You could have visited beforehand or happened upon the scene afterward. On the other hand, your DNA could have been left at the crime scene via a process called secondary transfer, where your DNA was transferred to someone else who then carried it to the scene.

"Prior to DNA, there was very little actual science being used in criminal cases. When DNA came about, we got a one-to-one comparison. Unless somebody screws something up, it should be accurate. It's based on legitimate science," explained Richard Torres, a criminal defense attorney and former DNA Unit attorney at the Legal Aid Society. "The trouble starts when you use this analysis on mixtures with other DNA samples or you try to extrapolate why someone's DNA is at a crime scene. My DNA is on a table because I sat and had dinner with someone the night before, but that doesn't mean I killed them the next day."

Imagine being charged with a crime based on a trace amount of DNA. The sample was analyzed using a DNA software that automates the analysis and interpretation of DNA samples. None of the people involved in your criminal trial know how the software actually works—not the judge, not the prosecutor, not your defense attorney, not even the forensic examiner. There is no other evidence against you, but the results of this software are treated as infallible.

This was the reality in thousands of criminal cases across the US over the last decade.

To make matters worse, when defendants try to get more information about the software, they are almost always denied on the grounds of trade secret privileges. This is not unique to DNA evidence either. Many of the surveillance technologies we've discussed, such as facial recognition, are also protected by trade secret laws.

These protections are especially troubling when applied to forensic algorithms because the analysis and interpretation of evidence, as well as the way it is presented in a court of law, is ultimately making decisions about an individual's liberty. Secret algorithms should not be permitted to make decisions like that, determining someone's guilt or innocence.

Often, only the software developers know how evidence derived from DNA mixture software came to be. Criminal defense teams have argued the prosecution should have to demonstrate the software was accurate and correctly validated. In fact, even the crime labs that rely on algorithms to analyze biometric data often do not have access to the information concerning how those algorithms work or where they pull their data from.

How accurate were the results? What was the known error rate? How exactly did the software work and could it accommodate defense hypotheses? Were the results really so dependable a jury could safely convict?

Companies market their DNA analysis algorithms without ever sharing the source code, except under very narrow circumstances. Complex DNA mixtures are analyzed by these same algorithms and used as evidence to support criminal convictions. The use of these forensic algorithms raises important questions of accuracy, fairness, and constitutional rights of criminal defendants, yet these uses have largely been permitted without any intervention from judges or the courts.

Representative Mark Takano (D-CA) introduced the Justice in Forensic Algorithms Act into Congress in September 2019 to address concerns about the lack of transparency that has plagued the use of these algorithms. The law would require source code be made available to criminal defendants in all cases in which such algorithms are used. The purpose of the act is to protect defendants' due process rights by prohibiting the use of trade secrets privileges to block access and challenges to this evidence (Congress.gov, 2021).

The act also calls upon NIST to establish two new programs: the Computational Forensic Algorithms Standards and a Computational Forensic Algorithms Testing program that would evaluate any forensic algorithms before approving them for use by federal law enforcement.

A newer version of the bill (HR 2438) was reintroduced in April 2021 and has been referred to the House Committee on the Judiciary as well as the Committee on Science, Space, and Technology. No other actions have been taken.

* * *

While forensic evidence has been scrutinized and criticized more frequently in the past decade, the history of forensic science in the courtroom is a legacy of junk science. Even when the American Bar Association (ABA) supported the use of DNA evidence, it urged caution in how statistics were interpreted.

The ABA advised lawyers not to oversell DNA evidence and recommended courts take the standards of the lab into account when considering DNA evidence. "Telling a jury it is implausible that anyone besides the suspect would have the same DNA test results is seldom, if ever, justified," the ABA said following a 1992 study from the National Research Council. This study raised concerns about the reliability of forensic labs and the statistical methods they used to form their conclusions (DeBenedictis, 1992).

Judges play an important role by evaluating the admissibility of evidence. "The problem is that once a judge decides whether evidence is admissible, that's now the law. We have a system that is treating these scientific questions like any other legal question," Torres said during our interview. "That's not how science works. Just because a prior judge made that decision doesn't mean it's the right decision."

Nearly two decades after the ABA's warning, the National Academy of Sciences (NAS) arrived at similar conclusions. In the now-famous 2009 report, *Strengthening Forensic Science in the United States: A Path Forward*, the NAS wrote, "No forensic method has been rigorously shown to have the capacity to consistently, and with a high degree of certainty, demonstrate a connection between evidence and a specific individual or source."

In other words, judges and juries have sometimes sent people to jail based on junk science.

Before joining the Legal Aid Society's DNA Unit, I overestimated the exonerative capabilities of forensic science because the Innocence Project often relied on DNA evidence to exonerate wrongfully convicted individuals. Yet as of 2021, the misapplication of forensic science contributed to 52 percent of wrongful convictions in Innocence Project cases. According to the National Registry of Exonerations, which tracks both DNA and non-DNA based exonerations, false or misleading forensic evidence was a contributing factor in 24 percent of all wrongful convictions nationally (The National Registry of Exonerations, 2021).

But every time someone gets released after decades in prison because they were wrongfully convicted based on misapplied science, we always hear the same rhetoric. *Oh, it's terrible how this evidence was improperly used to put them in prison. What a tragedy!* Currently, only a handful of states have laws to clarify a wrongfully convicted person can get back into court based on discredited forensic evidence.

This means forensic evidence and evidence interpretation are pain points for the scientific and legal communities alike. The field of forensic science is not the only one to blame. The legal community shares much of the blame for understanding so little about forensic evidence and continuing to rely on it when an individual's life and liberty are at stake. Blaming forensic science without also holding the law accountable will only exacerbate the problem.

CHAPTER 8

Beyond a Relative Doubt: Forensic DNA Databases & Familial DNA Searches

———

"The sins of the father are to be laid upon the children."
— SHAKESPEARE, *THE MERCHANT OF VENICE*

Genetic databases entered the national limelight after the arrest of the Golden State Killer in April 2018. At the time of his arrest, Joseph James DeAngelo was seventy-two years old and committed more than fifty rapes and twelve murders. His arrest was celebrated as a law enforcement victory. But the way law enforcement officials eventually found DeAngelo presents some valid concerns.

In addition to traditional detective work, law enforcement also turned to data from a crowdsourced genetic database

(Molteni, 2018). To find the Golden State Killer, police searched GEDmatch, a website that compiles raw genetic profiles shared publicly by their owners, and identified DeAngelo by using genetic information one of his relatives uploaded.

GEDmatch was created by the Mormon Church to share genealogical information. The primary purpose of the website appears to be for curious users searching for missing relatives or finding familial DNA matches to fill in family trees.

GEDmatch and its features for finding matches are mostly free. Users just have to create an account and upload copies of their raw DNA files from genetic testing services such as 23andMe and Ancestry. These two companies don't allow law enforcement agencies to access their customer databases unless they get a court order. However, GEDmatch has no such barrier. In fact, its opensource database of more than 1.4 million genetic profiles was available to the police searching for DeAngelo. Using sequence data from old crime scene samples, the police created a genetic profile for the Golden State Killer and uploaded it to GEDmatch. Using this profile, they were able to find a pool of relatives who shared some of that incriminating genetic material (Stanton, 2018).

After ruling out suspects, investigators narrowed down the search to just DeAngelo. During a police stakeout of DeAngelo's home, the police obtained his DNA from something he discarded. After running DeAngelo's sample against multiple crime scene samples, the police confirmed their suspicions. The DNA was a match.

The Golden State Killer eluded capture for over four decades. DNA evidence was ultimately what allowed the police to identify him. So what's the problem?

The Golden State Killer case reignited debates on the issue of DNA searches and the use of DNA evidence—with a twist. Should investigators use genetic databases to identify the *families* of suspects if doing so will lead them to the culprit?

Americans are divided. In a June 2020 survey of more than forty-two hundred US adults conducted by the Pew Research Center, 48 percent were okay with DNA testing companies sharing customers' genetic data with police. One-third said it was unacceptable. 18 percent were unsure (Perrin, 2020).

According to a report published in *Science*, by 2018, more than fifteen million people worldwide used direct-to-consumer DNA testing like 23andMe and Ancestry. Researchers estimated 60 percent of searches of a database with three million US residents of European descent could lead to a match with a third cousin or closer.

My worry is anytime law enforcement is granted a new technology or innovation, we often see the most extreme and overzealous uses. Like the various mass surveillance capabilities available to the police, familial DNA searches create a dragnet, bringing families and individuals with little to no link to a crime into the investigation.

And the cherry on top? In December 2019, Verogen, a company that specifically aids law enforcement agencies with forensic DNA work, bought GEDmatch. Verogen CEO Brett

Williams stated while GEDmatch users would retain the ability to opt out of searches by law enforcement agencies, such as those who helped identify the Golden State Killer, he also had a new vision for the website. GEDmatch would no longer just be for connecting family members via their DNA—the new focus is solving crimes (Aldhous, 2019).

While the changing vision raises alarms, one characteristic of GEDmatch remains similar to virtually any other genetic database: we don't know how reliable these databases are. Nongovernmental databases, whether public or private, haven't been vetted for law enforcement use, even though they're being used more and more as crime-fighting tools. The even greater concern is privacy. Most people who get their DNA tested for the fun of it or are curious about their ancestry and genetic predispositions probably don't think their genetic code might one day be scrutinized by the police. What about people who have never been tested?

Familial searches turn family members into suspects simply for sharing similar genes.

"The tension, though, is that any sample that gets uploaded also is providing information that could to lead to relatives that either haven't consented to have their information made public, or even know it's been done," Jennifer Mnookin, dean of the UCLA School of Law and a founder of its program on understanding forensic science evidence, said to *Wired* (Molteni, 2018). "That's not necessarily wrong, but it leads to a web of information that implicates a population well beyond those who made a decision themselves to be included."

The inheritance pattern of some DNA means close relatives share a higher percentage of alleles between each other than with other members of society (Steinberger and Sims, 2014). However, because familial DNA searches are based upon partial matches and probability estimations, this can lead to an increase in the number of people being investigated. Innocent or falsely accused individuals may also find themselves living under a constant cloud of suspicion if their DNA is stored in a database that can be used for familial searches.

"Someone can become a suspect because someone in their family ended up in a DNA database either because they had DNA stolen from them or they were previously convicted of a crime," criminal defense attorney Torres told me. "Suddenly, police are showing up at your job asking you questions about a crime because you have a likeness to someone who is in the database, even though you did nothing wrong."

Perhaps a more accurate way to think about familial DNA searches is it's a technique that narrows down the list of suspects rather than a technique that identifies an outright match.

"The idea that these tools can't possibly ever be wrong is so baffling to me. When we look at lie detector tests, bite mark analyses, and hair matching, barriers have been put up intentionally because, one by one, these things have been shown to be junk science," said Jerome Greco, a public defender in the Digital Forensics Unit of the Legal Aid Society, during our interview. "We've had junk science in the court system since before the founding of the United States. We never learn.

"Familial DNA searching seems so beyond what should ever be considered acceptable. It is a modern-day version of being held accountable for the sins of your father," Greco said. "Because a family member of yours was a possible match, it also becomes your issue. That seems completely unjustified."

Beyond privacy, another problem with the use of databases for familial DNA searches is the disproportionate impact it has on Black and Latinx individuals who are already trapped by the criminal justice system. Racial disparities in arrests and imprisonment ultimately translates into the disproportionate collection of Black and Latinx DNA, which gets taken and stored in federal and state databases.

In 2020, when NYU law professor Erin Murphy and attorney Jun H. Tong analyzed the racial composition of CODIS, the FBI's DNA database, they found people of color made up 48 percent of the database even though they constitute only 39 percent of the US population. More specifically, Black people made up about 34 percent of the genetic profiles, but only 13 percent of the US population is Black. In contrast, although white people make up 62 percent of the total population, they make up only 49 percent of the disclosed DNA database.

As of April 2018, twelve US states approved the use of familial searching in CODIS (Rainey, 2018).

In a May 2021 press release, the FBI revealed its national DNA database reached twenty million profiles.

This federal DNA database had humbler beginnings. When CODIS was first created in 1994, the original purpose of the database was to build upon the sex offender registry through the DNA collection of convicted sex offenders (Federal Register, 1998). Over time, that purpose expanded.

Today, all fifty states collect DNA from people convicted of felonies. According to the National Conference of State Legislature, as of 2018, eight states collect samples from juveniles. As of June 2021, twenty-nine states collect DNA samples from people who are arrested but not yet convicted of a crime (FBI, 2021). However, even when states limit DNA collection to those who are convicted of a crime, local databases, such as the forensic laboratory operated by the New York City Office of Chief Medical Examiner, may collect DNA samples of arrestees who have not been convicted (Brand, 2020).

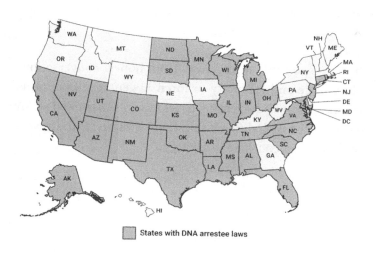

■ States with DNA arrestee laws

I can understand the value DNA databases can bring to legitimate crime-solving efforts. However, the privacy concerns and the risk of data abuse are too great a cost. Either way, I think it's critical for us to keep two issues in mind the next time we read about the police using a DNA database to solve a crime: how the database is used and how this use was decided.

While the collection and use of DNA in the criminal justice system is rapidly expanding, the understanding of politicians, jurors, and the general public has not kept up. There's been enough public discourse about the expansion of DNA databases, including the justice and fairness implications that accompany that expansion. Like any other tool, unfettered use can perpetuate racial disparities and chip away at civil liberties.

The criminal justice system has a tainted history of using state power to oppress communities of color, particularly Black communities. That legacy endures and manifests today. We have witnessed it for ourselves.

It is irresponsible to shy away from honest conversations about race and ethnicity in forensic genetics. Like other technological and scientific developments discussed so far, we are faced with difficult questions with no clear answers. Still, we must continue to ask them.

PART 4:

MAY IT PLEASE
THE ALGORITHM

CHAPTER 9

Algorithms Get
Their Day in Court

_____

"If you give me six lines written by the hand of the most honest of men, I will find something in them which will hang him."
— CARDINAL RICHELIEU

I wanted to be a lawyer since I was a sophomore in high school. A career in law first piqued my interest when I learned that I really enjoyed public speaking and advocacy through extracurricular activities like Model UN and a legislative simulation called Youth and Government, which was started by the YMCA's Civic Engagement initiative. My interest in technology goes even further back. When I was a child, I used to draw up concepts of flying cars and robots and was obsessed with computers and automation.

My interest in law and technology remained mostly separate until May 2016 when I read the famous ProPublica report "Machine Bias." For many, including myself, the report was illuminating. It revealed an algorithm claimed to predict a person's likelihood of committing another crime, and judges were using this prediction to decide how many years to sentence someone to prison for (Angwin, Larson, Mattu, and Kirchner, 2016).

ProPublica found the algorithm was especially likely to flag Black defendants as future criminals, labeling them as high-risk at almost twice the rate as white defendants. Meanwhile, white defendants were labeled as low-risk more often than Black defendants. The report also found the algorithm made unreliable forecasts about violent crime: only 20 percent of the people predicted to commit violent crimes actually went on to do so.

We are just starting to uncover this invisible threat. These algorithms further disadvantage Black people in a system that is already biased against them.

In 2014, Brisha Borden was running late to pick up her god-sister from school when she noticed an unlocked bicycle and scooter. Borden and her friend hopped on the bicycle and scooter and tried to ride them down the street in Coral Springs, a Fort Lauderdale suburb. The eighteen-year-old girls quickly realized they were too big for the bike and scooter, both of which belonged to a six-year-old boy. They immediately dropped the bike and scooter and walked away, but it was too late. A neighbor who witnessed what happened already called the police. Borden and her friend were arrested and charged with burglary and petty theft for the bicycle and scooter, which had a total value of eighty dollars. Apart from a few misdemeanors committed when she was a juvenile, Borden had no criminal record (Angwin, Larson, Mattu, and Kirchner, 2016).

One year earlier, forty-one-year-old Vernon Prater was arrested for shoplifting $86.35 worth of tools from a nearby Home Depot. Before that arrest, Prater had already been convicted of multiple armed robbery and attempted robbery charges, serving five years in prison. Compared to Borden, Prater was the more seasoned criminal.

However, something strange happened when profiles of Borden and Prater were entered into a computer program. This software predicted Borden—who was Black—had a high risk of committing a future crime. In contrast, Prater—who was white—was rated a low risk.

The algorithm got it wrong. As of 2016, Borden had not been charged with any new crimes. Meanwhile, Prater is serving an eight-year prison term for subsequently breaking into a warehouse and stealing about eight thousand dollars' worth of electronics, tools, and appliances (Angwin, Larson, Mattu, and Kirchner, 2016).

These algorithms are known as risk assessments. The risk assessment tool discussed in the 2016 ProPublica report is called COMPAS, which stands for Correctional Offender Management Profiling for Alternative Sanctions. It was created by the company Northpointe, now Equivant, and is used by US courts to assess the likelihood of a criminal defendant becoming a recidivist (Bornstein, 2017). COMPAS remains one of the most widely used risk assessments in the US.

Risk assessment instruments are designed to predict a defendant's future risk for misconduct. These predictions inform high-stakes judicial decisions, including whether to incarcerate an individual before their trial. Details of a defendant's profile are run through a risk assessment tool and it spits out a recidivism score. Courts and corrections departments across the US use algorithms to determine a defendant's "risk" with this score, which ranges from the probability an individual will commit another crime to the likelihood a defendant will appear for their court date (Tashea, 2017). A judge factors this score into a variety of decisions that can determine what rehabilitation services a defendant should receive, whether they should be held in jail before their trial, and how severe their sentences should be. While a low score generally results in a kinder outcome, a high score leads to the opposite.

These algorithms were designed to direct the allocation of resources. The idea was if an algorithm like COMPAS can accurately predict criminal behavior, resources can be more efficiently distributed, whether for rehabilitation or for prison sentences. Ultimately, risk assessment algorithms aspire to improve the accuracy of human decision-making, allowing for a better allocation of finite resources and a fairer and more just process for criminal defendants.

It's easy to see the appeal of risk assessments. A tool that can make high-stakes decisions in a rigorous, evidence-based manner, leading to better outcomes, may seem like an attractive prospect. However, the reality of risk assessment algorithms is more complicated.

I think the widespread use of criminal risk assessments in the judicial system is rooted in the problematic cash bail system in the United States.

Getting rid of the cash bail system probably appears on every criminal justice advocate's to-do list—and for good reason. Cash bail is used as a guarantee a defendant will return for a trial. The money is returned after they attend all of the required court appearances. If they miss an appearance, the bail is forfeited to the government (Onyekwere, 2021).

The US is one of the only countries in the world with a cash bail system that is dominated by commercial bail bond companies. In England, Canada, and other countries, agreeing to pay a defendant's bond in exchange for money is a form of obstruction of justice, like witness tampering or bribing a juror. In a *New York Times* article, John Goldkamp, a professor of criminal justice at Temple University, described the commercial bail bond system as "a very American invention." "It's really the only place in the criminal justice system where a liberty decision is governed by a profit-making businessman who will or will not take your business," Goldkamp said (Liptak, 2008).

Whenever any system operates with profit at its center, the poor suffer. It is no surprise people in prison and jail are disproportionately poor compared to the overall US population. In fact, more than 70 percent of the US jail population—over 555,000 people—haven't even been convicted or sentenced. Many are detained in local jails because they cannot afford to pay bail (Sawyer and Wagner, 2020).

The criminal justice system literally punishes poverty. The median bail amount for felonies is ten thousand dollars, which is the equivalent of eight months' income for the average detained defendant. As a result, people who can afford bail walk free while those who cannot are detained (Sawyer and Wagner, 2020). Bernie Sanders famously called for the end of "modern-day debtors' prisons" when he introduced a bill in 2018 to eliminate cash bail (Gambino and Jacobs, 2018).

The Black Lives Matter protests during the summer of 2020 also placed the cash bail system in the spotlight and introduced many people to the system for the first time. Most notably, the Minnesota Freedom Fund saw an influx of twenty million dollars in donations within four days after the police killing of George Floyd. Donations to bail funds during these important and widespread protests were a tangible way to show support to protesters who were facing police willing to use aggressive arrest tactics to quell legal dissent (Giorgis, 2020).

Over the past decade, more and more cities, counties, and states started to recognize the injustice of the cash bail system. In an effort to right decades of inequality between rich and poor defendants, states turned to an increasingly popular alternative: risk assessments, algorithmic tools that use predictive analytics (Henry, 2019).

When risk assessment tools were first introduced as an alternative to the cash bail system, prominent groups were quick to see their value.

In 2017, the American Law Institute, an independent organization that produces scholarly work to clarify and simplify US common law, approved a proposed final draft of the "Model Penal Code: Sentencing." This draft specifically recognizes the value of evidence-based sentencing with input from actuarial instruments that "estimate the relative risks that individual offenders pose to public safety through their future criminal conduct."

The First Step Act, signed into law in December 2018, mandates the development of a new federal "risk and needs assessment system." The Department of Justice in July 2019 released the Prison Assessment Tool Targeting Estimated Risk and Needs (PATTERN) with the goal of reducing recidivism and connecting incarcerated people with rehabilitative services (Grawert, 2020).

Today, risk assessment tools are used in almost every state in the US, as well as in the federal system, in some form. While early implementation of risk assessments was focused on pretrial decisions, judges soon started using them in sentencing and parole decisions as well.

Unfortunately, risk assessment tools are engendering the same results of the system it was meant to replace.

For example, originally, the Pretrial Justice Institute (PJI) strongly advocated for the implementation of these tools. However, in February 2020, PJI reversed their position, stating they "now see that pretrial risk assessment tools, designed to predict an individual's appearance in court without a new arrest, can no longer be a part of our solution for building equitable pretrial justice systems."

One week later, Public Safety Assessment, a widely used risk assessment developed by Arnold Ventures LLC, formerly the Laura and John Arnold Foundation, released a statement in which they clarify "implementing an assessment cannot and will not result in the pretrial justice goals we seek to achieve" (Carter and Shames, 2020).

But criminal risk assessments don't just impact pretrial bail or detention decisions.

A 2016 Wisconsin Supreme Court case, *Loomis v. Wisconsin*, underscores many of the concerns with risk assessment tools. The petitioner, Eric Loomis, was convicted of fleeing an officer and driving a car without the owner's consent. The case challenged the State of Wisconsin's use of COMPAS, which was used to sentence Loomis to six years in prison.

First, Loomis argued the court's use of COMPAS violated his due process rights, specifically the due process right to be sentenced based on accurate information. He argued because he was denied full access to how COMPAS calculated his risk score, he was unable to scrutinize the accuracy of all information presented at his sentencing. The Wisconsin Supreme Court disagreed, stating it was sufficient to observe the COMPAS inputs and outputs.

Second, Loomis contended a court's consideration of the COMPAS output "amount[ed] to sentencing based on group data rather than an individualized sentence based on the charges and the unique character of the defendant." The court disagreed, arguing the sentencing decision was not solely determined by the COMPAS score.

"The risk score alone should not determine the sentence of an offender," Wisconsin's assistant attorney general, Christine Remington, said during state Supreme Court arguments in the Loomis case. "We don't want courts to say, 'This person in front of me is a ten [out of ten] on COMPAS as far as risk, and therefore I'm going to give him the maximum sentence.'"

When the case was appealed to the US Supreme Court in 2017, it declined to hear the case.

Risk assessment tools generally raise three concerns: lack of individualization, lack of transparency, and, of course, bias.

The US judicial system has historically made discriminatory and biased decisions. However, judicial proceedings are open to the public and judges explain the reasoning for their decisions in published opinions. These are subject to examination and criticism not just by other judges and lawyers, but by the public.

The same cannot be said about risk assessments. Companies that create and sell risk assessment tools frequently hide information behind trade secret claims (Wexler, 2018). This lack of transparency makes it virtually impossible for defendants to appeal algorithm outputs. How do you challenge a decision when you don't even know how that decision was made? How do you cross-examine an algorithm in a court of law?

With respect to individualization concerns, we have seen this problem come up in other predictive algorithms. A risk assessment's prediction about any individual is going to draw on historical information of not just that individual, but of *similar* individuals. I think of predictive algorithms as working like a mirror, reflecting society's biases and priorities. ACLU chief data scientist Horowitz offered an even better analogy during our interview.

"They're more like funhouse mirrors of society. They can amplify certain pieces of the way that things were in place before the algorithm was being used and they can distort a lot of things that we take to be true under this auspice of being scientific and data-driven."

As they currently exist, risk assessment algorithms are yet another way to sanitize and legitimize oppressive systems. It distracts from actual problems affecting low-income and minority communities, like defunded schools and inadequate access to healthcare.

Algorithmic tools cannot replace sound policy or much-needed reforms to the criminal justice system. Similarly, the push for a more just and equitable criminal justice system cannot stop at reforming algorithmic tools. It must challenge the humanmade institutions and systems they support.

"People only pay attention to whether or not the algorithm itself is biased, but increasingly, the thing that I'm afraid of is not that the algorithm is biased, but when you put that algorithm in front of a judge, the judge actually becomes more biased than they were before they had the algorithm,"

Horowitz said. "Ultimately, the algorithm isn't encouraging judges to release more people. It's just allowing the judge to make the same decisions they would have made before, but now they can say, 'A risk assessment instrument told me this person was a high risk, so I had to detain them.'"

CHAPTER 10

Behind Closed Source: How the Law Keeps Algorithms Hidden from Us

---

"I see, these books are probably law books, and it is an essential part of the justice dispensed here that you should be condemned not only in innocence, but also in ignorance."

— FRANZ KAFKA, *THE TRIAL*

In 2014, the US attorney general at the time, Eric Holder, warned scores from risk assessment algorithms could introduce bias in the court system. He called on the US Sentencing Commission to study the use of these algorithms. "Although these measures were crafted with the best of intentions, I am concerned that they inadvertently undermine our efforts to ensure individualized and equal justice." He added, "They may exacerbate unwarranted and unjust disparities that are already far too common in our criminal justice system and in our society."

The sentencing commission did not, however, launch a study of risk scores.

If they did, the commission would have found a major problem afflicting predictive algorithms in the criminal justice system: historical crime data. This reliance on historical crime data is so problematic because the data is the result of biased and racist policing practices. Making future decisions based on past mistakes does not make a system fair. By codifying the criminal justice system's discriminatory and racist practices into a technical system, criminal risk assessments ensure these biases would be replayed in perpetuity.

According to Northpointe's "Practitioner's Guide to COMPAS," published in 2015, "an individual's level of risk is estimated based on known recidivism rates of offenders with similar characteristics." In other words, judicial decisions that rely on COMPAS algorithms are also informed by historical group tendencies for misconduct. But don't both humans and algorithms learn from past behavior? It's worth noting predictions about anyone—whether that prediction is made by an algorithm, a judge, or anyone else—are naturally tethered to historical behavior of similar individuals.

Sharad Goel, a computer science professor at Stanford University researching criminal sentencing tools, dislikes the opacity in these tools but believes the critique cuts both ways. "Everything that happens in the criminal justice system involves a human in some way, and every time a human is involved, there's always this potential for bias," Goel said in an article published in *The Atlantic*. "We already have black boxes making decisions for us all the time, but they just happen to be sitting in black robes" (Thompson, 2019).

But people don't want to make decisions that might get them in trouble or make decisions that are just flat-out wrong. Rebecca Wexler is a law professor at UC Berkeley who has researched, written, and spoken extensively about trade secrets, technology, and criminal justice. "It's easier for a judge to rely on a risk assessment instrument and point to that to explain their sentencing decision or their pretrial incarceration decision. They'd rather have that degree of removal so that they don't have to be in the direct line of responsibility if something goes wrong," Wexler told me about the judiciary's use of risk assessment algorithms. "I think for people who are in decision-making positions, it is to their advantage to develop a view that the machines are objective, that they aren't just reflecting prior human decisions."

How did these risk assessments even end up in the courtroom, though? What makes these risk assessment tools "algorithmic?"

Risk assessments have actually been a part of the US criminal justice system since at least the 1930s (Henry, 2019). However, for decades, they were *clinical*; they primarily relied on experts' judgment, like psychologists, social workers, or probation officers. The result of the assessment ultimately depended on the person conducting it.

On the other hand, *actuarial* risk assessments are based on statistical models and do not rely on human judgment—sort of. Humans still have to create the model, determine the input variables, and assign weights to those variables. The statistical models themselves may be as simple as linear or logistic regression models or as complex as a machine learning algorithm.

An algorithmic risk assessment is just a subset of actuarial risk assessment. An algorithmic risk assessment typically relies on software to perform a series of calculations to produce the final risk score.

For example, the COMPAS Violent Recidivism Risk Scale is calculated using the following equation:

$$s = a(-w) + a_{first}(-w) + h_{violence}w + v_{education} + h_{noncompliance}w$$

Here, s is the violent recidivism risk score, a is the defendant's current age, a_{first} is the defendant's age at their first arrest, $h_{violence}$ is the defendant's history of violence, $v_{education}$ is the defendant's vocational education level, and $h_{noncompliance}$ is the defendant's history of noncompliance. Northpointe explained the weight multiplier, w, is "determined by the strength of the item's relationship to person offensive recidivism that we observe in our study data" (Northpointe, 2015).

That's the thing, though. This is a lovely equation and all, but we don't actually know how COMPAS weighs each variable. That's because Northpointe considers the weights of these input variables to be trade secrets. "So if one of those inputs is wrong, it's impossible to tell how it affects your final score," said Wexler. "Without the ability to prove that the final score gives a distorted picture of your life, you can't convince anyone to fix it."

Risk assessments also weigh factors such as a defendant's socioeconomic status, family background, employment status, neighborhood crime, and criminal history. However, by relying on historical crime data, criminal risk assessments pick out patterns *correlated* with crime rather than *causing* crime. For instance, if an algorithm found low income was *correlated* with high recidivism, it would leave a police officer, prosecutor, or judge none the wiser about whether low income actually *caused* crime.

Risk assessments do just that: turn correlations into causal scores. Furthermore, other data inputs such as zip code or family criminal history can be proxies for race, resulting in racial biases seeping into the output even when it is not explicitly used by the algorithm. When considering the history of racism in the US criminal justice system, it is no surprise the country's leading risk assessment algorithms predict Black people are nearly twice as likely as white people to be labeled a high risk but not actually reoffend (Yong, 2018).

Risk assessments rely on AI to sift through data and make decisions about a criminal defendant. Generally, the two most controversial issues with algorithmic risk assessments are the choice of inputs and the quality of the data.

The choice of inputs tells two stories: what the developers hope to predict and what data developers believe will make accurate predictions. Likewise, the quality of the data that goes into the model reveals the priorities of the people or institutions who collect it (Henry, 2019).

The use of arrest data to train predictive algorithms does not paint an accurate picture of criminal activity. Arrest data is used because it is the data police department's record. However, arrests do not necessarily lead to convictions. Data about arrests and convictions are abundant, but arrest data say more about the behavior of law enforcement and courts than about criminal defendants.

"In the case of pretrial risk assessments, the people who make these tools predict rearrest and failure to appear before the court," said Horowitz, chief data scientist at the ACLU, during our interview. "These risk assessments are essentially supporting detention or release decisions based on really bad proxies for the things that court systems are supposed to care about, and therefore, enabling a continued use of excessive pretrial incarceration."

A risk assessment used to inform a sentencing decision should predict whether the person being sentenced will go on to commit a new crime at some point after the end of their supervision. It may seem intuitive for that decision to be based on whether people with similar profiles historically went on to commit crimes. Although estimated data exists, those estimates are incomplete. Furthermore, the data that gets chosen is usually whatever is easiest to quantify rather than the fairest (Bornstein, 2017).

Many risk assessments, including COMPAS, use rearrest within two years as a definition of recidivism. A tool designed to inform sentencing decisions should ideally predict the likelihood the person being sentenced will commit a new crime—not the likelihood the person will be arrested again (Morgan and Truman, 2018). "They're predicting rearrest. Rearrest is a reflection of where cops are spending their time. It's not a reflection of violence," Horowitz said. "All they do is predict rearrest, which pretty much means they're just predicting discrimination against Black people and poor people."

A crime will often occur without anyone being arrested. On the other end of the spectrum, people are routinely arrested without ever committing a crime. The likelihood someone will be arrested reflects as much about policing as it does about the behavior of the person being sentenced (Henry, 2019).

A common criticism of proprietary risk assessments is since the algorithms they use are considered trade secrets, they cannot be examined by the public and affected parties, presenting potential due process concerns.

Loomis, for instance, didn't know exactly how the COMPAS model worked, but he knew it took gender into account. When he argued that was discriminatory, the court disagreed, highlighting the model's inclusion of gender made it more accurate. Although Loomis's challenge failed, that limited information he had about the model allowed him to challenge it, demonstrating the importance of transparency, especially for algorithms that play a role in such high-stakes decisions like sentencing someone to prison (*State v. Loomis*, 2016).

Government agencies rarely ever write their own risk assessment algorithms. Instead, private businesses design and sell these proprietary tools to the government, resulting in a "black box" problem. This means only the original developers and, to a limited degree, the purchaser can see how the software makes decisions (Tashea, 2017). Since most risk assessment algorithms are proprietary, these systems remain opaque and prevent the public from seeing what variables and factors are used to calculate risk scores. Worse yet, because there are virtually no transparency requirements for risk assessment tools, many jurisdictions have adopted these tools without first testing their validity.

"This isn't how trade secrets law is supposed to work. Intellectual property exists because we think that people will be more likely to invest in new ideas if they can stop their business competitors from freeriding on the results," Wexler explained. "If trade secret law is designed to stop business competitors from stealing information and we apply those laws to shield information from defense attorneys, what does that say about defense attorneys?"

Defense advocates have been calling for more transparency methods because they are unable to challenge the validity of the results at sentencing hearings. Because the public has no opportunity to identify problems with these algorithms, it cannot present those complaints to judges or government officials. Without an opportunity to challenge the algorithms, the public and governments actors alike are unable to influence policy changes.

This complete lack of transparency makes it practically impossible to disentangle the use of risk assessments from other factors that affect crime or incarceration rates. However, some studies have shown signs courts' use of risk assessment tools has had a small, positive impact. For instance, a 2016 study conducted by the University of Pennsylvania's Department of Criminology found no evidence a machine learning tool used in Pennsylvania to inform parole decisions jeopardized public safety—that is to say, the tool correctly identified high-risk individual who shouldn't be paroled—and some evidence it identified nonviolent people who could be safely released (Berk, 2016).

Bail decisions have traditionally been made by judges relying on intuition and personal preference. In a study of pretrial hearings in Cook County, Illinois, researchers found judges spent an average of just thirty seconds considering each case (Heaven, 2020). Under those conditions, it's safe to say judges are making snap decisions that are at least somewhat informed by personal biases.

So to reduce potential arbitrariness, judges in some cities receive scores generated by an algorithm that rate a defendant's risk of skipping trial or committing a violent crime if released. Judges are still free to exercise discretion, but algorithms bring some consistency and evenhandedness to the process. In Virginia, nearly twice as many defendants were released without increasing pretrial crime. Similarly, in New Jersey, adopting algorithms in bail decisions contributed to a 16 percent drop in its pretrial jail population with no increase in crime (Corbett-Davies, Goel, and González-Bailón, 2017).

However, if the tool was designed for punitive purposes, then it will be used to punish. For example, Human Rights Watch reported in Santa Cruz County, "judges agreed with 84 percent of the 'detain' recommendations, but just 47 percent of 'release' recommendations." In Alameda County, judges disregard release recommendations and set bail for as much 75 percent of all defendants labeled "low-risk" (Human Rights Watch, 2017).

In March 2019, Idaho became the first state to enact a law specifically promoting transparency, accountability, and explainability in pretrial risk assessment tools. The law prevents trade secret or intellectual property defenses and requires public availability of "all documents, data, records, and information used by the builder to build or validate the pretrial risk assessment tool." Perhaps most crucial to the legal process, the law enables defendants to review all calculations and data that went into calculating their risk score (Lipton, 2019).

"Ultimately, we're building an algorithm for something that shouldn't have an algorithm," Horowitz said about risk assessments. "The data is a reflection of what is happening in society, but once you implement the algorithm, it becomes an amplification system." As an algorithm takes information that was previously not used, that new information becomes part of its historical data. So as information is fed into the algorithm, it amplifies problems that already exist.

CHAPTER 11

Digital Shackles: How Parole Apps Put Prison in Your Pocket

———

"There is no greater tyranny than that which is perpetrated under the shield of the law and in the name of justice."
— MONTESQUIEU, *THE SPIRIT OF THE LAWS*

One of the first times I really noticed ankle monitor bracelets was when Martha Stewart was released from prison in 2005. She was required to wear one after five months in a minimum-security prison for lying to government investigators looking into a personal stock sale she made in 2001. About two years after Stewart's release, Paris Hilton was also fitted for an ankle bracelet and put under house arrest after being sentenced for violating her probation. However, ankle bracelets have been used long before their association with law-breaking celebrities.

In the 1960s, identical twins Robert and Kirk Gable were graduate students at Harvard. While studying social psychology under B.F. Skinner and Timothy Leary, the Gable twins repurposed war surplus missile-tracking equipment to track young adult offenders. "Our idea was, gosh, if you can train pigeons to play ping-pong, you ought to be able to get kids to show up for therapy on time," Robert said in a 2007 interview with *Wired*.

While the devices emitted radio signals to communicate where the offenders were, the Gable twins viewed the purpose of these devices as a form of positive reinforcement. They came up with the idea of giving rewards to offenders when they were where they were supposed to be, such as a drug treatment session, school, a job, or a parole meeting. If an offender was compliant, the device would signal to them they were eligible for a simple reward—a free haircut, pizza, concert tickets—all to inspire better behavior. "We wanted to apply operant conditioning to human social problems," Kirk said in the same interview.

But that's not how things turned out.

With overcrowded jails and the high cost of incarceration, many states turned to electronic monitoring as a cost-effective way to send people home and free up jail space. The government uses electronic monitoring to track an individual's location and make sure they comply with the terms of their release. Terms can range from being at home every night by a certain time or avoiding specific places.

Thanks to this technology, the prison cell just comes home with you.

Today, ankle monitors and other electronic monitoring devices no longer use radio signals to detect whether someone is home or moving around a city. Many devices use GPS and cell tower signals to give more precise locations. Monitors for DUI offenders can even detect blood alcohol levels through a person's sweat (Anderson, 2014).

This technology can deprive their wearers of their liberties in invasive and unexpected ways. "It pretends to be an alternative to incarceration, but it's actually a form of incarceration," said James Kilgore, a former fugitive and social justice activist who writes widely on issues pertaining to mass incarceration (Solon, 2018). In some cases, the government covers the cost of the technology. After all, one of the main drivers for the proliferation of electronic monitors is saving money on expanding prison facilities.

However, in many counties, fees for the wearer range anywhere from five to forty dollars per day. That's not even including the initial setup fee, which can be between 175 and two hundred dollars (Kilgore, 2015). Some parolees must wear ankle monitors for years; others are forced to wear ankle monitors for a lifetime. Years of electronic monitoring use puts parolees deeper and deeper in debt.

According to a 2016 brief from The Pew Charitable Trusts, around fifty-three thousand people were supervised with monitors in 2005. But by 2015, that number reached more than one-hundred-twenty-five thousand people. That's nearly a 140 percent increase in just ten years.

Some people view the rise in electronic monitors as an appealing alternative to mass incarceration, mostly because it allows people to serve time while still providing for their families (Paunescu, 2019). However, as we know by now, developments in technology do not occur in a vacuum. To understand the widespread use of electronic monitors and their staying power, we need to take a look at another mechanism in the criminal justice system: probation.

Probation in criminal law is a period of supervision over an offender, ordered by the court instead of serving time in prison. An offender on probation is ordered to follow certain conditions set forth by the court, often under the supervision of a probation officer. During the period of probation, an offender faces the threat of being incarcerated if found breaking the rules set by the court or probation officer. On the other hand, parole is the early release of an incarcerated person who agrees to abide by certain conditions.

Four and a half million people in the US are under probation or parole in what is commonly referred to as "community supervision." That's nearly twice the number of people incarcerated in prisons and jails combined (Jones, 2018). Despite the massive number of people stuck in this system, parole and probation have only recently started to receive public scrutiny.

Probation and parole systems are often plagued with injustices, setting people up to fail with long supervision terms, burdensome restrictions that affect the ability to seek employment opportunities, and increasingly invasive surveillance. Probation, in particular, often results in people being sent back to jail.

Parole apps, boosted by the COVID-19 pandemic, are increasingly being used in state criminal justice systems and federal immigration courts to track people while they await trial or are on probation or parole. They are easier to install than GPS ankle bracelets, which must be worn around the ankle at all times. Parole apps also come with a variety of analytics features and are much cheaper. In fact, in some jurisdictions, the person being monitored must pay a daily fee instead of the justice agency purchasing the service.

In some jurisdictions, the pandemic led to the rapid adoption of parole tracking apps for broad populations of offenders. For example, for several months in 2020, Illinois canceled in-person meetings and forced parolees to install SmartLINK, a monitoring app that collects real-time data on probationers (Feathers, 2021).

According to detention data published by the Immigration and Customs Enforcement (ICE), in 2020, the agency monitored 28,581 people through GPS ankle bracelets and 23,804 through SmartLINK. As of May 2021, there are 32,838 people using bracelets and 32,794 using SmartLINK. "It is not a substitute for detention, but allows ICE to exercise increased supervision over a portion of those who are not detained" based on factors like "criminal and immigration history; supervision history; family and/or community ties; status as a caregiver or provider; and other humanitarian or medical consideration," according to the agency's website (Feathers, 2021).

This recent data indicates probation and parole monitoring apps are not necessarily replacing GPS ankle bracelets. Instead, both devices are expanding side by side. Critics point out the data-gathering and predictive analytics used in some tracking apps raise concerns about false positives that may lead to arrests for technical violations of probation or parole conditions.

For example, SmartLINK uses predictive analytics to calculate a person's likelihood of absconding and what their travel patterns say about their access to "risk locations." Meanwhile, Shadowtrack, another parole app, claims to have voice recognition algorithms that are capable of detecting whether a person has been using alcohol or drugs. "We have some proprietary software built in that can detect some slurs in speech, and so forth, that would just maybe warrant a follow-up," Robert Magaletta, chief executive of Shadowtrack, said in an interview with *The Guardian* (Feathers, 2021).

Chaz Arnett, a law professor at the University of Maryland, sees probation tracking apps as another example of tech-washing conservative prison reform efforts with a trendy AI label while still enriching the private incarceration industry.

"It doesn't do anything to get at the fact that the criminal justice system itself is geared toward punishment, especially when you're talking about underprivileged communities of color," Arnett said in an interview with *The Guardian*. "And once you get into these practices where you're pulling data, biometric data, and these companies are using that data to further monetize their programs and experiment, often it's people of color who are having their data extracted from them. This valuable commodity is literally the body of Black individuals" (Feathers, 2021).

But before an app puts the parole agent in someone's pocket, a judge must decide whether that person gets parole. For an increasing number of parole decisions, judges aren't even calling the shots anymore—algorithms are, and most incarcerated people don't even know it.

Almost every state in the US uses risk assessment tools to make parole determinations.

With respect to recidivism, most people come back to prison because of technical violations, such as missing a curfew, lack of employment, or failing to report for a scheduled office visit. "We don't have information about whether or not those people would have come back to prison in the absence of excessive technical violations," Horowitz said during our interview. "So all an algorithm is doing is really predicting whether or not you're going to be a bad parolee, but not whether or not you're going to harm somebody in your community."

Using historical data to train risk assessment tools could mean machines are merely mimicking the mistakes of the past. Populations that have historically been disproportionately targeted by law enforcement—especially low-income and minority communities—are at risk of receiving high recidivism scores. As a result, the algorithm could amplify and perpetuate biases and create even more biased data, creating a feedback loop between biases in the real world and algorithms.

"You'll hear a lot of people say, 'Well, we can just fix the algorithm,' and you can statistically remove bias from an algorithm," Horowitz said. "But you're not going to remove bias from the judges who use the algorithm and you're certainly not going to deal with the fact that the algorithm is just keeping the same number of people incarcerated as you had before you instituted that algorithm."

We need to think about how we treat people, even if they've done something wrong. Our technology will do what we tell it to do. If it is designed to punish, then it will do just that. If we develop technology that is exonerative or restorative, it can do that too.

"We were trying to find a way to avoid the hostility and judgment that goes with treatment of juvenile offenders," Robert said to *Wired* in 2007.

"People still haven't realized that anger and hostility are counterproductive," Kirk added.

As we consider alternatives to incarceration, we also need to critically examine the core purpose of those alternatives. They cannot be half measures. If we are serious about doing away with a carceral system that is strictly punitive, we need to look to solutions that provide individuals with real opportunities to rejoin their communities and achieve a form of justice that is centered on rebuilding accountability and trust.

PART 5:

TROUBLESHOOTING THE PROBLEM

CHAPTER 12

Futureproofing Our Civil Liberties

———

"The future belongs to those who prepare for it today."

— MALCOLM X

American democracy is a delicate thing. History reminds us shocking events are followed closely by rhetoric and action that prioritize collective security in place of individual liberty.

Just two months after the attack on Pearl Harbor, President Roosevelt issued Executive Order 9066, resulting in the internment of Japanese Americans. During the Cold War, a secret presidential directive created the National Security Agency (NSA), which intercepted millions of telegrams to and from the US, placed millions of law-abiding Americans on watchlists, and circulated private communications to the FBI and CIA. After the September 11 attacks, the US government ramped up targeted surveillance of Muslim communities, expanding the terrorist watchlist and infiltrating mosques.

It's easy (and perhaps even comforting) to think of these civil liberty abuses as products of misguided hysteria and paranoia. But that would undermine the very real dangers of unprotected data and unchecked surveillance, particularly when enabled by today's technology.

"At the most big-picture level, what we need to do is make sure that technology and developments in technology don't take away our liberties and our rights," Esha Bhandari, deputy director of the ACLU's Speech, Privacy, and Technology Project, said during our interview. "To the extent that we have these innovations, we need to make sure they enhance our liberty and improve our ability to live out our values of equality, freedom, and privacy. Oftentimes, technology is a force for diminishing those rights."

The US Capitol attack that took place on January 6, 2021, was a flashpoint. Facial recognition, geotagged photos, social media profiles, location data, and surveillance cameras were critical to bringing this violent mob to justice. I've had countless conversations about how these insurrectionists had it coming and how this is the "right" way to use AI. Still, I can't help but think about how the data collected on January 6 is a demonstration of the threat AI-enabled tools pose to our collective civil liberties. A threat that affects civilians, insurrectionists, and everyone in-between.

In 2006, British mathematician and entrepreneur Clive Humby coined the phrase, "Data is the new oil." He argued, "Data is just like crude. It's valuable, but if unrefined, it cannot really be used. It has to be changed into gas, plastic, chemicals, and so on to create a valuable entity that drives profitable activity; so must data be broken down, analyzed for it to have value."

This idea caught on like wildfire. Marketing departments, tech companies, governments, policymakers, and news media alike still refer to this idea and even rely on it as a strategy. "Data is the new oil" quickly achieved the status of "holy writ" (Naughton, 2021).

In a May 2021 blog post, designer Matt Locke put forth a better metaphor for data:

"All these metaphors imagine public data as a huge, passive, untapped resource—lakes of stuff that only have value when it is extracted and processed. But this framing completely removes the individual agency that created the stuff in the first place. Oil is formed by millions of years of compression and chemical transformation of algae and tiny marine animals. Data is created in real time as we click and swipe around the internet. The metaphor might work in an economic sense, but it fails to describe what data is as a material. It's not oil, it's people."

Data is the largest collection of human thought and behavior ever recorded. It's not some passive resource waiting to be disturbed or exploited. It's our history.

If we start thinking about data and ourselves as one in the same, we might also start to demand more safeguards from technologies that use it as nothing more than just fuel.

We are now at a crossroads. AI has real-world impacts and consequences on people, institutions, and culture. The technology has reached a point where its downsides in our day-to-day lives are becoming increasingly difficult to avoid and stop.

What happens if AI is cemented in our daily lives before its flaws are fully addressed?

"It's very hard to tear down a bridge once it's up," Robert Moses said.

* * *

An algorithm may give an impression of objectivity and neutrality because its decisions appear to be the product of a logical, unemotional machine rather than a human with biases and preconceived notions. However, the algorithm is a humanmade product. Its decisions are the result of data from the real world, the consequences of our history, our policies, and our mistakes.

But whose responsibility is it to put a stop to biased and unethical AI? There are three groups:

- The government, specifically lawmakers and regulators, as well as the law itself.

- The private sector, including AI developers, tech companies, and other corporations.

- The public, such as activists, organizers, researchers, and so on.

Lawmakers and regulators, at their best, have been slow to set rules and standards to regulate AI. At their worst, government institutions, such as the FBI and police departments, actively use AI in dangerous and invasive ways.

AI is improving medical procedures and technologies, cutting costs across various industries via automation, and personalizing user experiences online. At the same time, using this technology at scale also creates new problems: discrimination, violence, and loss of privacy.

Many of the regulatory agencies in the US, established to address problems in the age of industry and manufacturing, are in dire need of an update to keep up with businesses in the digital age.

While government, especially at the federal level, has been playing a constant game of catch-up, I think one group bears the largest share of responsibility for identifying and remedying biases in AI systems: developers and tech companies.

AI developers make decisions about what data is used to train the AI model. This includes making sure the data is representative and not skewed toward a specific demographic. I would also argue developers have a responsibility to make sure their models don't include any discriminatory parameters like gender, age, ethnicity, or socioeconomic status. Ultimately, a model should be designed in such a way it does not encode existing biases in the real world.

Beyond its design, an AI model should also undergo rigorous testing (and ongoing monitoring and auditing once it is unleashed upon the world). Facial recognition software, for example, should be accurate for faces of various ages, ethnicities, and genders.

Tech companies make decisions about the purpose of a product as well as who it is ultimately marketed and sold to. While government actors are supposed to be beholden to the needs and wants of the public, directing our discontent at tech companies can be more impactful.

While there are countless reasons to be skeptical of corporations, I do believe there are opportunities for some private actors to close the regulatory gap left by public institutions. Creating a regulatory market, for instance, may create a competitive and compelling environment for private actors to pressure tech companies to develop more ethical and accountable products.

Finally, we have the public. We stand to lose the most if we allow flawed technology to take root in our communities. People misidentified by facial recognition may be forced into the police's crosshairs, surveillance technology keeps tabs on who attends protests, and algorithms maintain the carceral system.

"People care a lot about these issues. It's a nonpartisan issue. Nobody wants computers controlling their lives, especially if those computers are biased," said Liz O'Sullivan, the CEO of Parity, an algorithmic fairness company, in our interview. "We are now finding out more and more, and the more complexity you add to a model, there is a higher likelihood that it's going to discriminate against somebody."

On a more fundamental level, fighting unethical and biased AI also requires us to come to terms with our part in its creation. Remember how data is people? Well, the data we create—like the profile photos we post online, the Amazon Ring footage we unknowingly send to local police departments, and the genetic information we willingly hand over to private companies—is ultimately being used against us. It's going to take our collective action to change that.

Luckily, we can stand on the shoulders of giants. Inspiring activists from different fields have dedicated their careers to not only highlighting the problems that plague AI, but litigating important cases to protect civil liberties, informing the masses, and advocating for new legislation and policies.

The task before us is daunting, but we live in an exciting time. AI offers a historic opportunity to detect and fix bias at an unprecedented scale. If we remind ourselves about how we are the very data being used against us, we can also take ownership and reclaim what is ours.

The following chapters will take a look at each group—the government, the private sector, and the public—to take stock of what is being done in each space, as well as what can (and should) be done going forward.

CHAPTER 13

The Wild, Wild West:
The Role of Government

———

"Nobody needs to justify why they 'need' a right: the burden of justification falls on the one seeking to infringe upon the right... Arguing that you don't care about the right to privacy because you have nothing to hide is no different than saying you don't care about free speech because you have nothing to say."

— EDWARD SNOWDEN

In September 1958, sixty thousand residents of Fresno, California, became test subjects in one of the boldest experiments in capitalism. They received a small, thin, rectangular piece of plastic in the mail. Residents' names and addresses, a seemingly random series of numbers, and an expiration date were printed on this plastic rectangle. Above all of that information, in all capitalized letters, read "BankAmericard." Today, we know BankAmericard as Visa (Nocera, 1994).

Over the course of the next twelve years, banks mailed credit cards to random people until the US government outlawed the practice of mass card mailings. By 1970, over one hundred million credit cards were in circulation (Nocera, 1994).

In the early 1970s, the largely unregulated credit card industry experienced rampant fraud, costing credit card companies millions of dollars. Credit card companies regularly held cardholders liable for fraudulent transactions even if their cards were lost or stolen. As a result, Congress passed the Fair Credit Billing Act in 1974 to limit cardholder liability.

This protection not only increased public trust in credit cards as a new payment method but also encouraged growth and innovation. Since credit card companies could no longer just pass fraud losses onto cardholders, they developed one of the earliest commercial applications of neural networks to detect anomalies in a customer's card usage, reducing their fraud losses (McCarthy, 2020).

Law should help direct the development of emerging technology. Sound regulation that guides new technology, like of the credit card industry, can protect consumers and drive innovation. However, policymakers opted to give players in the tech industry free rein to develop and deploy AI as they saw fit. At both the local and federal level, even government use of AI has essentially remained unregulated. If the 1974 Fair Credit Billing Act turned the credit card industry into a more civilized society, then AI has remained the wild, wild west.

Despite widespread law enforcement and governmental use of AI, there are virtually no federal laws governing the use of this technology. Federal agencies have no clear democratic mandate nor any explicit legislative authority to use AI. As we have seen, algorithms developed to make important decisions continue to codify and perpetuate bias while staying shielded from public scrutiny.

Renée Cummings is an AI criminologist, AI ethicist, and the first data activist in residence at the University of Virginia's School of Data Science. "The technology is leading the law. So much of this technology, like facial recognition and big data policing, is being used without the direction of the law," Cummings said to me. "The lack of a legal perspective in the use of this technology gives our law enforcement a lot of leverage, and they are using these tools without the understanding that this technology could impact communities and make some communities that are already vulnerable more vulnerable."

The opaqueness of governmental AI systems has prompted many to demand disclosure-style transparency. In recent years, academics, technologists, and activists alike have called for greater transparency into the inner workings of AI models. Looking under the hood can help to mitigate issues of fairness, discrimination, and trust. However, simply revealing the biases and problems in AI systems won't be enough.

Frank Pasquale is a law professor at Brooklyn Law School and expert on the law of AI, algorithms, and machine learning. Pasquale is also the author of *The Black Box Society* and *New Laws of Robotics*. As one of his students, I consider myself very lucky to have easy access to his thoughts and insights on algorithmic accountability and the role of regulation in the AI space.

"My biggest worry in this area is that the AI regulation is going to go the way of finance regulation," Pasquale told me during a conversation about my book. "Most finance regulation is just disclosure. Financial regulations don't try to shape what we invest in or shape the financial industry more actively. They're just telling banks to make sure people understand what they're getting into."

Disclosure requirements are an after-the-fact solution. These types of regulations would do little to nothing to actually direct how AI technology can be used more ethically. Pasquale proposes we regulate AI less like banks and more like cars. "We can't just buy a car and drive off on the road with it. You've got to actually register it with a state where you have demonstrated that you know how to drive," Pasquale said. "There has to be an ongoing check, similar to how we have to renew our driver's licenses or have car inspections. We need to require institutions to get a certificate of compliance before using AI for certain applications. That, to me, is the ultimate solution."

* * *

Another mechanism that ensures the continued black boxing of the criminal justice system is something we may not immediately consider: intellectual property. AI developers typically claim information about their tools, such as forensic analysis software or risk assessments, are trade secrets and refuse to disclose details to criminal defendants or their attorneys.

Judges are traditionally protective of property rights, including intellectual property. As a result, what we're seeing a lot of times is judges protecting intellectual property rights instead of the rights of criminal defendants. This creates a situation where criminal defendants and their attorneys have no way of arguing against an algorithmic output. How do you defend yourself against something you cannot see or understand?

There are already serious information asymmetries in criminal trials. The information gap between prosecutors and defendants is widened by the trade secret shield wielded by corporations that produce and sell forensic analysis algorithms and other tools presented as evidence in court. If you are a private company that wants to do business with the government, you should understand you are doing business in a democratic society with a set of rules and norms that protect the due process rights of individuals, including those who are accused of crimes.

Nate Wessler is a deputy director with the ACLU's Speech, Privacy, and Technology Project, where he focuses on litigation and advocacy around surveillance and privacy issues. In 2017, he argued *Carpenter v. United States* in the US Supreme Court, which established the Fourth Amendment requires law enforcement to get a search warrant before requesting cellphone location data from a person's cellular service provider, like AT&T or Verizon. I had the opportunity to ask him about his thoughts on the blurred line between private sector markets and law enforcement.

"If a business is so afraid that their secret sauce is going to leak out in a way that's going to subject them to competitive disadvantage, maybe they should go into a different line of business where they're not contracting with law enforcement," Wessler said. "When decisions about people's life and liberty are on the line, I think it should be a no-brainer that people should have access to all the information they need to test the evidence being used against them, even if it is a proprietary algorithm."

When I spoke to law professor Rebecca Wexler, who focuses much of her research on trade secrets and criminal justice, and asked about her opinions on this issue, she argued trade secrets should not be privileged in criminal proceedings but also recognized the importance of intellectual property rights. After all, if we disclose trade secret information to the public, then it's no longer a secret.

"I've advocated for a middle ground where trade secrets should not entitle vendors to entirely withhold relevant evidence from criminal defendants," Wexler said. "We can still protect legitimate intellectual property interests in those technologies by using protective orders to limit the subsequent dissemination of that information to the public. Once you have disclosure under a protective order, if there's an issue like a flaw that is relevant to judicial determination, then the public can move to have a second inquiry. This is called a motion to unseal, where some of that information might then have to be revealed to the public, but it's a different step of the process."

Intellectual property protections are generally viewed as a legal mechanism that enables innovation and development of valuable technology. Businesses have used trade secret claims to prevent the disclosure of proprietary information to competitors. That may be true in many industries. However, the reason why the inner workings of a lot of the technology I've discussed in this book are such well-guarded secrets is because these companies don't want their controversial or flawed technology (oftentimes both) to be scrutinized by the public.

"It's going to be a lot harder for a company to sell its algorithm to police if experts retained by defense attorneys are able to poke holes in it, like pointing out coding errors or finding that the product performs fine in laboratory settings but goes off the rails when you subject it to real-world applications," Nate Wessler pointed out. "What the companies really prefer is that the only information out there are their own claims or their marketing materials."

Take ShotSpotter for example. The company claims human voices do not trigger its gunshot detection system. However, in 2012, two men were convicted of murder after part of their argument was picked up and recorded by ShotSpotter. The recording was used as part of the prosecution's case. Court documents reveal while ShotSpotter is attuned to the sound of gunfire, its listening and recording system runs twenty-four-seven and recordings are stored for up to three days (Goode, 2012).

"With the introduction of AI systems in policing and the criminal legal system, there's a privatization of a lot of decisions. In the past, these decisions would be made by a public servant, a human," Clare Garvie from the Center on Privacy & Technology at Georgetown Law said to me. "Those decisions are now made by an algorithm or by a system that was developed by a private company. It's marketed in very slick ways to get people to think that it's more accurate and less biased than a human decision-making process. The system falls far short of that, but there's this tendency to not only not explain how these systems work, but also not challenge how they work. There is this inherent trust in a system that just genuinely doesn't warrant that trust."

When a lone criminal defense attorney is arguing against the prosecutor, the district attorney's office, crime labs, software companies, and AI developers, that attorney is really arguing against massive institutions with a tremendous amount of power and resources, as well as a supposed expertise and knowledge in building these tools. When a single person is going up against institutions, a judge will almost always side with the institutions.

"We need the public to know what technologies are being deployed by police, by prosecutors, by crime investigators, by judges, by parole officers. We need the public to know how technology and private vendors are influencing those practices that are done in our name," Wexler said.

* * *

There is a need for greater transparency about how AI systems are developed, the assumptions that are made in their design, and how frequently they are assessed and updated.

Although transparency alone will not necessarily reduce the likelihood of bias, it does make possible an extremely valuable bias mitigation solution: audit by outside researchers (Kehl, Guo, and Kessler, 2017).

Algorithmic auditing has emerged as a key strategy to expose systematic biases embedded in software platforms. Audits are valuable because they can improve the general understanding of these systems and provide more information about the inputs, as well as their respective weights. This transparency can also enable auditors to identify algorithmic bias and suggest fixes to the system.

Lawmakers and researchers have advocated for algorithmic audits, which involve dissecting and stress-testing algorithms to see how they work and whether they're adequately performing their intended goals or producing biased outcomes (Ng, 2021).

In an algorithmic audit, an independent party may evaluate an algorithmic system for bias, as well as accuracy, robustness, interpretability, privacy characteristics, and other unintended consequences. The audit would identify problems and suggest improvements or alternatives to the developers (Guszcza et al., 2018).

"Auditability is critical to the development and deployment of AI. It serves as a checks and balances mechanism," Renée Cummings said. "You don't ever want to get to the point where harm has been done and then there's nothing you can do, so a critical space for redress when it comes to technology is having audits and impact assessments done throughout the development lifecycle."

In 2016, the Obama administration published a report on algorithmic systems and civil rights that called for the development of an algorithmic auditing industry. A key concern about criminal risk assessments is the lack of transparency. Legal and technical experts have called for greater transparency about how these algorithms were designed, the assumptions that were made during their development, how their inputs were weighed, and how frequently they were assessed and updated (Executive Office of the President, 2016).

However, hiring an auditor still isn't common practice since there is no incentive or obligation to do so. Companies want to avoid scrutiny or even potential legal issues that may result from that scrutiny, especially for products they sell to public and private entities.

"Lawyers tell me, 'If we hire you and find out there's a problem that we can't fix, then we have lost plausible deniability and we don't want to be the next cigarette company,'" said Cathy O'Neil, founder of O'Neil Risk Consulting and Algorithmic Auditing, Inc. (ORCAA) and author of *Weapons of Math Destruction*. "That's the most common reason I don't get a job" (Ng, 2021).

Companies may use algorithmic auditing to make real improvements, like eliminating bias, but they might not. There are currently no industry standards or regulations that hold auditors or companies that use them accountable. Although transparency alone will not necessarily reduce the likelihood of bias, it does make possible an extremely valuable bias mitigation solution: audit by outside researchers. Audits are valuable because they can improve the general understanding of these systems and provide more information about the inputs, as well as their respective weights (Ng, 2021). This transparency can also enable auditors to identify algorithmic bias and suggest fixes to the system.

"I think auditing and testing in operational conditions is incredibly important and that's really what's lacking with technology like face recognition, but I don't think it's sufficient because these are all sociotechnical systems," Clare Garvie said. "These are all systems that have a human component. If we ignore the human component, it tacitly assumes that the technology is going to get to a point where the error rates are going to drop off or the accuracy is going to get to an acceptable level."

It doesn't matter how good the algorithms are if the humans using them do not also improve. Beyond addressing conscious and unconscious biases, humans using this technology must also be properly trained. For example, facial recognition outputs rely on human analysts' ability to conduct unfamiliar face identification. Without the proper training, humans can make incorrect determinations or introduce their own biases.

"We can't divorce the risks of the tools from the intent of the people using them and how it's being used. I think that's the part that's often overlooked," Garvie said. "Develop a tool and someone's going to find a way to misuse it or use it in a way that violates people's rights."

However, until a federal law can harmonize rules about privacy and ethical AI, we may have to count on state-level regulations and moratoriums or even some private actors to fill that gap.

Operating within the confines of a capitalist society, industries and private corporations need to have an incentive to evolve, change, and regulate. As it stands, the AI industry has a lot of incentive to keep this space unregulated—if not from a legal liability standpoint, then certainly from a business standpoint.

The Food and Drug Administration (FDA) sets standards for food and drugs while determining whether products should be approved for consumer use. Financial institutions are subjected to auditing and regulatory reporting requirements set by regulatory agencies like the Federal Reserve Board and the Securities and Exchange Commission (SEC). The National Highway Traffic Safety Administration (NHTSA) conducts crash tests on new vehicles and rates their performance. What prevents AI—a technology so pervasive and with such an immense potential to do harm—from being scrutinized in a similar fashion?

The benefit of a federal law is it would create a standardized approach to regulating AI. There is value in this uniformity since the current regulatory approach has been extremely patchwork and hyperlocal. In the absence of federal regulations, cities and states have led the charge in reining in government use of AI systems, relying heavily on moratoriums or wholesale bans on technologies like facial recognition and predictive policing.

"We're going to continue to see the expansion of state and local bans that will limit the capacity for these technologies to gain even more of a foothold in the individual communities," S.T.O.P. founder Albert Cahn said during our interview. "These efforts will build out this national consensus until we finally have enough communities that categorically ban facial recognition, automated license plate readers, or predictive policing that we have the basis to then move forward with a ban on these technologies at the federal level."

In Garvie's view, rules governing the use of these technologies will not come from the federal government. "The federal government might produce guidance, but I think it's more likely that this is going to be a question that's kicked to the courts," Garvie said. "Courts may say something like face recognition is akin to another biometric forensic tool like fingerprinting and decide the parameters based on the Rules of Evidence."

In 2019, a group of Democratic lawmakers introduced the federal Algorithmic Accountability Act, which had not only required companies to audit their algorithms, but also to address any bias issues the audits identified before they're put to use (Robertson, 2019). The idea was if the auditing agency spotted disparate impact, then that algorithm wouldn't be sold or deployed.

The bill never made it to a vote.

Senator Ron Wyden (D-OR) said, in February 2021, he plans to update and reintroduce the Algorithmic Accountability Act with Senator Cory Booker (D-NJ) and Representative

Yvette Clarke (D-NY). The 2019 version of the bill did not clarify whether the federal law would set auditing standards, but it would require companies to address shortcomings identified during these audits.

"I agree that researchers, industry, and the government need to work toward establishing recognized benchmarks for auditing AI, to ensure audits are as impactful as possible," Wyden stated. "However, the stakes are too high to wait for full academic consensus before Congress begins to take action to protect against bias tainting automated systems. It's my view we need to work on both tracks" (Ng, 2021).

The Health Insurance Portability and Accountability Act, more popularly known as HIPAA, was signed into law by President Clinton in August 1996. HIPAA was created to address several issues, including the continuity of health coverage for people who lose their jobs, safeguarding against healthcare fraud, protecting private health information, and developing industry-wide standards. However, a federal law may not have been signed into law if the healthcare industry did not also want guidance at the federal level.

"I think what was driving HIPAA was the health care industry itself wanted guidance on how to share digital medical records in a safe way. The problem with AI is that it's run wild and the industry doesn't really feel like they need guidance yet," law professor Frank Pasquale said when I asked him about why it's been so difficult to regulate the AI industry. "I think that the way to think about it is every government official who has some capacity or obligation to develop a political vision for regulation should have in mind a view as to what AI is going to be used for in their agency and how it can go wrong. That's the culture change we really need."

We cannot get caught up in the talismanic way technology is so frequently talked about. Our technology should not just be innovative—it must be ethical. If we start thinking of our civil liberties as a matter of dignity rather than a privilege, we will begin to demand more responsible technology, especially with respect to uses that impact the public.

"The market is a beast, but you can still impose ethical standards on it. A lot of it comes down to how the RFPs are written," postdoctoral researcher and former police officer Brandon del Pozo said to me.

An RFP, or "request for proposal," announces a project, describes the specifications of that project, and solicits bids from different contractors to complete it. Almost every government contract at all levels in the US goes through an RFP process or bidding process, especially in the surveillance technology space. "A city could write an RFP that requires the winning bidder to disclose their algorithm to the public or hold a public hearing where the scope, nature, and business process of the surveillance technology is open to inspection from the public," del Pozo said. "The private sector wants these government contracts, so the government being proactive and setting these requirements can actually shed some light on what's going on inside that box."

But is there enough of an incentive for politicians or city officials to do that? Sure, it may be the moral or ethical action to take when the technology is designed to be used on the public, but is there enough pressure from the public to trump the political agendas of the few in power?

"It's a political process. We are seeing jurisdictions banning the use of facial recognition or putting severe limits on governmental use of that technology. These companies ultimately have to gain the trust of the government," said del Pozo. "Transparency is one of a few ways to gain that trust."

In addition to passing new laws and regulations, the judiciary has an important role to play too, particularly since we have seen this technology play a critical role in how evidence is presented during trials, as well as how judges make determinations about how harsh a sentence should be. Still, it can be a challenge for the judicial system to keep up with the speed of technology.

Esha Bhandari, deputy director of the Speech, Privacy, and Technology Project at the ACLU, believes what we need is for courts to be willing to be the first to decide a question about how technology should be applied, even when it is new technology. Historically, courts have been reluctant to acknowledge the new capabilities of AI, particularly in the surveillance space, resulting in a too-slow expansion of privacy protections for everyday civilians.

"Litigation can't be the only tool because it's just too slow of a process to keep up with the pace of technology. Litigation can take months or years. In the meantime, people's rights are implicated and the technology get entrenched," said Bhandari. "I think one of the problems we've seen is that the approach for new technology, particularly technology used by government or law enforcement, is 'adopt the technology first, deal with the consequences later' rather than a framework that presumes that new technology that affects people's rights cannot be used until it's gotten the go-ahead from courts or from laws passed through a democratically accountable process."

* * *

In any movement, it can be easy to place responsibility on the individual. Climate change comes to mind. Corporations and even governments frequently push accountability onto individuals. How often do you hear messages about how *you can do your part*? The reality is individuals can at most be responsible for their own behavior. However, governments have the power to pass legislation that compels industries and individuals to act sustainably. In fact, a 2017 Carbon Disclosure Project report found just one hundred companies have been responsible for over 70 percent of global emissions since 1988. If companies are responsible for so much of global greenhouse gas emissions, why is our first response to blame individuals for their consumption patterns?

We need to think about the regulation of AI in a similar way. It can be overwhelming if we think of data privacy and algorithmic bias as a problem for individuals because so many of us need to use certain tools to survive or rely on smartphones for work. Beyond individual tools, there are also technologies we have no control over, particularly surveillance technology. In many cases, it is impossible for us to individually opt out of sharing our data.

"At this point, if you drive on a highway, you can't even pay tolls without the government taking a photo of your car and license plate," said Bhandari. "I think it's easy to say this is about individual-level choices when in fact it's about society-wide choices."

The government's continued use of flawed technology is a threat that is already here, and it's only becoming more and more dire. Governments at the local, state, and federal levels need to take this threat seriously. If creating ethical and productive AI for social good is a priority for our elected officials, there are ways to involve groups that care about ethical AI.

Establishing fellowship programs or contracts for public interest technologists, requiring public-facing technologies to meet regulatory standards, and creating platforms for communities to assess and scrutinize those same technologies can rebuild trust with the public while guiding innovation toward a future that is focused more on transparency and accountability.

Until then, we need to demand our elected officials do what many cities and some states are already doing: pause the rollout of untested and potentially harmful technologies. Our communities should not be made into laboratories for tech companies.

CHAPTER 14

Flipping the Script: The Role of the Private Sector

———

"There are two ways of constructing a software design: one way is to make it so simple that there are obviously no deficiencies, and the other way is to make it so complicated that there are no obvious deficiencies. The first method is far more difficult."

— C. A. R. HOARE

In January 2020, *The New Yorker* published an article by Louis Menand titled "The Changing Meaning of Affirmative Action." In his opening paragraph, Menand wrote:

"The terrible paradox of the civil rights movement is that outlawing racial discrimination made it harder to remediate its effects. Once we amended the Constitution and passed laws to protect people of color from being treated differently in ways that were harmful to them, the government had trouble

enacting programs that treat people of color differently in ways that might be beneficial. We took race out of the equation only to realize that, if we truly wanted not just equality of opportunity for all Americans but equality of result, we needed to put it back in. Our name for this paradox is affirmative action."

While researching for this book and thinking about potential solutions, I kept coming back to concepts related to diversity and inclusion, particularly affirmative action.

The term was first introduced during the Kennedy administration about sixty years ago. President John F. Kennedy's Executive Order 10925 created a committee with a vague mandate intended to communicate the administration's commitment to fairness in employment. Affirmative action was used to instruct federal contractors to ensure companies the federal government did business with did not discriminate on the basis of race. Because the committee lacked any real enforcement mechanisms at the time, affirmative action meant to communicate to companies they should not discriminate, but not much else (Menand, 2020).

This committee would become the Equal Employment Opportunity Commission, or EEOC, which was created following the Civil Rights Act of 1964 for the purpose of enforcing Title VII, which prohibits discrimination in employment on the basis of race, color, religion, sex, or national origin.

At its core, the purpose of affirmative action is to offset a group's historical disadvantages by adjusting a decision-making process to be more favorable toward that group (Humerick, 2020). Generally, this adjustment is achieved by incorporating that group identity as a positive factor in the decision-making process, then rebalancing the weight of the other factors (Rozen, 2018). Affirmative action is an acknowledgment humans are flawed and biased.

The history of affirmative action is intertwined with the history of American race relations, just as the history of American race relations is intertwined with the history of America. As Menand aptly wrote, "It is the eternal bone in the national throat" (Menand, 2020).

Not everyone supports affirmative action. I can understand peoples' discomfort with what appears to be preferential treatment or wrapping one's head around the idea the way to end discrimination is by discriminating. But affirmative action is extremely important considering our country's history. It's impossible to have an honest and legitimate conversation about American history without acknowledging race and racism.

Independent of what I think, though, affirmative action worked. It turns out racial diversity doesn't happen on its own when institutions aren't forced to do so. Who knew?

Law professor Melvin I. Urofsky, in his book *The Affirmative Action Puzzle*, wrote about a 1981 report the Reagan Labor Department commissioned on increases in hiring among Black people. It found from 1974 to 1980, the rate of minority employment in businesses that contracted with the federal government, and were therefore subject to affirmative action requirements, rose by 20 percent. In businesses that did not contract with the government, the rates were 12 percent.

This finding was so contrary to what the Reagan administration had been saying about affirmative action the Labor Department hired an external consulting firm to check its own work. When the firm came back saying the methodology and conclusions were valid, Reagan refused to release the report, allowing politicians to go on telling the public that affirmative action didn't work.

Affirmative action requires institutions to have some degree of demographic consciousness. To address historical disadvantages and biases, a system must actually classify members of society, recognize the disparate experiences of each group, and adjust accordingly. Could such an approach be applied to algorithms? Could algorithmic affirmative action mitigate algorithmic bias?

Back in 2011, the Council to the Members of the American Law Institute already proposed the simplest form of affirmative action for risk assessments at sentencing: low risk scores should be given more weight than high risk scores. Low risk scores are also more often accurate than high risk scores because, from an actuarial perspective, attempts to identify people of low recidivism risk are more often successful than attempts to identify people who are unusually dangerous (Reitz and Klingele, 2011).

Prioritizing the accuracy of low risk scores would also likely have positive externalities along racial lines, disproportionately benefitting Black defendants with high scores. Discounting high risk scores would create a ripple effect, leading judges to assign shorter sentences based on high risk scores, thereby reducing racial disparities at sentencing (Humerick,

2020). Ultimately, the benefits of affirmative algorithms are rooted in tying bias mitigation to historical discrimination that can be empirically documented and attributable to the deploying entity (Ho and Xiang, 2020).

Algorithmic affirmative action would provide a counterbalance to bias in the data. In theory, another way to accomplish this goal for risk assessment algorithms would be to use differential risk thresholds. For example, three arrests for a Black person could indicate the same level of risk as two arrests for a white person.

This approach was examined in a study published in May 2020 by Jennifer Skeem, a psychologist and professor at UC Berkeley, and Christopher Lowenkamp, a social science analyst at the Administrative Office of the US Courts. Skeem and Lowenkamp tested different options for removing bias in algorithms that assessed the risk of recidivism for about sixty-eight thousand participants, half Black and half white. They found the best balance between races was achieved when algorithms actually took race explicitly into account and assigned Black people a higher threshold than white people for being deemed high-risk.

Unfortunately, many of the strategies that would address algorithmic bias issues conflict with the US Supreme Court's rulings on equal protection, namely the push for "anti-classification," or remaining "blind" toward categories like race, gender, and religion.

In *Parents Involved in Community Schools v. Seattle School District No. 1*, a 2007 Supreme Court decision, Chief Justice

John Roberts stated, "The way to stop discrimination on the basis of race is to stop discriminating on the basis of race."

Alternatively, Justice Sonia Sotomayor, in the Court's 2014 *Schuette, Attorney General of Michigan v. Coalition to Defend Affirmative Action, Integration, and Immigration Rights and Fight for Equality By Any Means Necessary* decision, stated, "The way to stop discrimination on the basis of race is to speak openly and candidly on the subject of race and to apply the Constitution with eyes open to the unfortunate effects of centuries of racial discrimination."

I agree with Justice Sotomayor's approach. Shying away from frank conversations about bias and prejudice will only allow these things to fester in the AI and tech space.

The original intent of affirmative action was to ensure federal contractors did not discriminate on the basis of race. The same spirit could be applied to AI systems—whether developed by public institutions or private companies—to ensure public-facing technologies do not also have a discriminatory effect when deployed in our communities.

It goes without saying the concept algorithmic affirmative action may be an uncomfortable one. People and organizations developing these algorithms would be manipulating the data to forgive a proportion of crimes because of the perpetrator's race. The thought of holding members of different groups to different standards cuts against many people's sense of fairness, even if it is done in a way that is supposed to address historical injustices.

A "colorblind" approach can seem appealing, but a more critical look will quickly reveal how many laws and policies have failed communities of color by not considering their experiences and the history they endured.

An approach that is "blind" to any category ultimately brushes it under the rug—and "out of sight, out of mind" cannot be what we strive for in this space. An approach that neglects to account for race is convenient and comfortable because it is inaction. The opposite of active and deliberate racial discrimination is not willful ignorance—it must instead be active and deliberate remediation.

* * *

Another simpler and more practical way to address algorithmic bias is diversity.

First, the data used to train algorithms must be diverse and representative. If the training data are more representative of some groups of people than others, the skew in the data results in a skew in the results as well. In practice, the AI's predictions may be systematically worse for groups that are either unrepresented or underrepresented in the training data.

Representation in the training data cuts both ways, though. For example, when Joy Buolamwini experimented with facial recognition, she found the low accuracy for darker-skinned faces was the result of their underrepresentation in the training data. Alternatively, when Clare Garvie and her team evaluated law enforcement facial recognition networks, they found Black people were more likely to be singled out due to their overrepresentation in mugshot databases. Biased outcomes can be the result under both circumstances.

Beyond the training data, the teams developing AI models should also be diverse. Diverse teams are better at identifying bias in AI and anticipating a product's impact on diverse communities. Developing and scaling AI requires more than just technical expertise. Having empathy for users as well as members of the public who may be more likely to have interactions with the product is key, especially for companies that care about widespread adoption of their AI solutions.

I believe our government should really reflect its constituents. Tech companies should be held to a similar standard. The ideal AI development team should resemble the people who will be impacted by the final product. Developers and tech companies aren't just making products to be sold. More and more frequently, the AI tools they build encode the priorities of the government and have real, often life-altering consequences.

Diversity cannot be relegated to a corporate buzzword. Companies that actively confront it in the development stage as well as the recruiting stage of an AI product's lifecycle will be better for it.

* * *

An unregulated market can be dangerous for businesses and consumers alike. However, if given the choice, tech companies would rather self-regulate than be subjected to regulation or law. That's actually what played a part in the birth of privacy policies. They were a voluntary measure taken by companies to promote privacy practices while staving off further regulation. The idea was to convince lawmakers self-regulation works and no additional rules were needed. For tech companies, this self-regulation was largely successful and has kept regulators at bay.

Of course, we can't have tech companies build, market, and sell AI and leave them to their own devices (pun intended). But a lack of political cohesion in the federal government has caused legislation to lag and oversight to be overlooked. But what if governments didn't have to do it alone? What if we could take some of the positive traits of markets—competition, incentive, and transparency—and apply them to a new private sector regulatory framework?

I think that's why some find a "regulatory market" to be such a viable option. I also agreed with Liz O'Sullivan when she told me, "We're not going to see immediate action from the government in the way that changing a policy at Amazon can protect Black people nationwide from being falsely accused of crimes."

A regulatory market "combines the incentives that markets create to invent more effective and less burdensome ways to provide a service with hard government oversight to ensure that whatever the regulatory market produces, it satisfies the goals and targets set by democratic governments" (Hadfield, 2020).

Under this regulatory market framework, governments set goals rather than enact laws or regulations. Independent companies fill the regulatory role by developing new ways to meet those government-set goals. These independent private regulators would also compete to sell regulatory services to tech companies, which the government can mandate (Clark and Hadfield, 2020).

To prevent this from being a race to the bottom, with independent companies competing to be the most lenient regulator, the government takes on the responsibility of regulating the regulators. For example, a government-issued license may be required to compete in this market, and if goals are not met or if private regulators cheat, licenses are revoked. Regulating a more controlled market like this also means the government is less likely to get overwhelmed by a larger tech industry (Clark and Hadfield, 2020).

* * *

When I met with O'Sullivan, the CEO of Parity, I was especially interested to hear her thoughts on the role of corporations and whether it makes sense for corporations to hold their peers accountable. "What Parity does is look for ways to automate model risk processes. We think that every model, especially the higher impact ones, have a lot of potential for harm and they're not getting the kinds of ethical considerations, or even practical considerations, about the ways these models fail," O'Sullivan explained. "When they fail, which is inevitable, what will they do to the public? Will they harm us? Will they create or sustain further inequities?"

But what incentive do corporations have to develop more ethical models or fix unethical ones?

"The incentive is they don't want to get sued into oblivion," O'Sullivan said. "Algorithmic discrimination has been proven to be illegal even when unintentional. But I think the biggest tool that we have is public backlash against algorithmic discrimination. It's a loss of revenue and loss of reputation for these companies, who serve the public at large."

Accountability to the public is an important feature of a democratic society. A politician's voting history is public record so their decisions and priorities can be scrutinized by interested constituents. A judge's opinions are public record so their reasoning and conclusion can be evaluated by their peers and the public alike.

AI developers and tech companies are increasingly involved in creating and selling technology to public institutions. This technology is ultimately used on us, yet decisions about the design of an AI model, how variables are weighed, biases that may have been identified and ignored, and a million other factors are hidden away behind conference room doors or lost in Bay Area open-plan offices. I think developers and tech companies have become private policymakers. Their decisions have profound effects on communities across the country but none of the accountability or scrutiny.

While there are companies and other private sector actors who can rein in unethical and dangerous technologies, I'm not too keen on relying solely on the altruism or discipline of the private sector, especially when algorithms used for law enforcement or criminal justice purposes have tremendous impacts on life and liberty. At the end of the day, a company's goal is to generate revenue.

However, creating a new and competitive regulatory market that entices private regulators and delegate tech industry expertise to private regulators allows the government to focus on holding a smaller group of actors accountable. Developing a regulatory market may also provide public interest technologists with an entry point into the private sector without abandoning long-term activist goals. Instead, a regulatory market may provide the resources and platform to make positive changes on a shorter timeline.

Regardless, the fact remains: the self-regulation tech companies have enjoyed for so long cannot persist. Just as diversity in the workplace didn't begin to happen until the federal government stepped in with affirmative action, we cannot expect tech companies to suddenly prioritize diverse datasets and safer AI tools.

CHAPTER 15

Beyond Technology: Expecting More from AI

———

"The problem, really, is that while humanity continues to experience huge leaps in technology, we experience no equivalent leaps in our ethical capacity. In the never-ending arms race between technology and ethics, technology always wins. Researchers who tally the results of this immortal race have a name for it: history."

— DAVID J. MORRIS, WRITER AND FORMER
MARINE INFANTRY OFFICER

Have you ever waited somewhere when you suddenly spotted someone yawning, then, before you knew it, you felt compelled to yawn too? You may have heard about contagious yawning. In fact, according to one study, the likelihood of yawning increases sixfold after seeing someone else yawn (Provine, 1989). A phenomenon called social mirroring is likely responsible for yawn contagion. Social mirroring is when organisms imitate the actions of others.

The saying "monkey see, monkey do" refers to learning something by mimicry, generally without understanding why it works or concern about the consequences. In the wild, monkeys imitate each other to learn techniques to communicate and survive. Researchers have also made faces at baby monkeys, such as sticking out their tongues or smacking their lips, and found baby monkeys copied these facial expressions. The researchers believe, because baby monkeys cannot see their own faces, they imitate the adults around them.

Through a process like social mirroring, monkeys learn from the environment they are a part of and ultimately assimilate the norms and behaviors of that environment.

We've built machines to do just that.

Algorithms work by following rules and unemotional logic. If one thing is clear, though, it's this doesn't make them immune to baseless bias. If the rules, or the data used to create those rules, are biased, the output of the algorithm will reflect that. As AI, neural networks, and machine learning become more advanced, this problem of algorithmic bias will also become increasingly more complex and more difficult to detect and fix.

I'd even go as far as to say algorithms are discriminatory by nature. An algorithm's very purpose, especially in the criminal justice context, is to categorize people and data and spit out results that are consistent with preexisting patterns.

Data is also inherently biased. Why do companies and governments collect data? Why is our data so valuable? If each and every one of us was the same, treated the same, acted the same, and thought the same, then there would be no insight to gain from our data. Data had no value.

The algorithms are not the issue, at least not the most important one. We have to look beyond the technology. If we focus exclusively on solving technological problems, we miss out on the deeper, systemic problems that must also be addressed. The solution cannot be perfectly accurate, unbiased technology.

"It's a systems problem much more than an algorithms problem," ACLU chief data scientist Aaron Horowitz said to me. "There's been far too much emphasis on the algorithms themselves and not enough emphasis on the impact of their use or even the systems that they support."

For instance, with exposure to a complete, diverse, and representative data set of facial images, facial recognition systems could theoretically be rid of bias. However, a system that classifies people with perfect accuracy can be even more dangerous. If inaccurate facial recognition is already leading to wrongful arrests, imagine what it can do when the government can specifically target certain groups. It wouldn't be the first time a well-intentioned tool was repurposed to maintain oppressive systems.

"You can probably fix those biases in a short period of time, and facial recognition will probably get close to 100 percent accuracy and we won't have these bias questions anymore," Bhandari explained. "But we still need to ask ourselves if this is an enterprise that's compatible with civil rights and civil liberties. I think the bias question is a huge one, but I think one of the bigger picture questions is whether we are asking AI to do something that's just fundamentally incompatible with human rights, or are we asking AI to do something that we actually think really has to be done by a human."

All this time, we've just been asking our technology to *automate* human decisions when we should really be asking it to *augment* those decisions. Saying "humans are biased" is an objective truth on par with "the sky is blue." Automating human decision-making processes only serves to preserve and expand bias. We've cut corners for the sake of "innovation" and "disruption," so why haven't we demanded more aspirational technology?

The commercial satellite imaging industry, enabled by the over seven hundred surveillance satellites in Earth's orbit, sells images to buyers in the public and private sectors alike. But satellite imagery combined with machine learning has also been used to predict poverty by analyzing nighttime lighting since it is a proxy for economic wealth (Jean et al., 2016). ShotSpotter, designed to detect gunshots, has been found to record ambient noise as well, including conversations. In Central Africa, researchers used audio recorders and AI to predict not only elephant behavior, but also poacher activity (Temple-Raston, 2019).

Whenever someone makes claims about how something will improve society, it's important to listen with a healthy amount of skepticism. However, just as technology is not intrinsically objective or fair, it is also not in and of itself biased or unethical. *We* make it so.

Ayanna Howard, a roboticist, educator, and dean of the College of Engineering at Ohio State University, believes we have to actively design distrust into AI systems to make them safer. "If I'm over trusting these systems and these systems are making decisions that have different outcomes for different groups of individuals...we're not creating systems that augment the inequities we currently have," Howard told the *MIT Technology Review* (Hao, 2021).

Going forward, there are four key questions we must ask whenever technology is used on the public.

IF AI IS INTRODUCED TO THIS PROCESS, WHO ARE THE WINNERS AND LOSERS?

AI ushered in the age of automation. Computers can make decisions faster than ever. That doesn't make them more fair. Every time new developments are introduced, there will be winners and losers. If we take a closer look at developments that prioritize efficiency over justice, we will see the winners and losers are almost always the same.

Think back to Robert Moses and the impact he had on New York. Who benefitted from his housing and urban development projects? Who ultimately suffered as a direct result of those same projects?

When various industries implemented automation and other labor-saving technologies, corporations saved money as the cost of production fell. Blue-collar workers lost their jobs.

Our transition into a cashless society will likely be more convenient for consumers who can afford credit cards or mobile payment methods, but lower-income individuals will inevitably be excluded.

Similarly, when decisions are outsourced to machines, poor people and people of color stand to lose the most. A wealthy white person is far less likely to be targeted by law enforcement. As a result, wealthy white people are also far less likely to be affected by untested forensic analysis software and biased risk assessment algorithms.

WHAT IS THE PURPOSE OF THIS TECHNOLOGY?

We also need to think about what purpose an algorithm is serving, particularly in the criminal justice context. "The algorithm just encodes policy choices. An algorithm is only going to tell you what you ask it to tell you," Esha Bhandari from the ACLU said to me. "If you say to an algorithm, 'I want to lock up 50 percent of the people who are arrested. I want to deny them bail,' then an algorithm will come up with a way to do that, but you've made that policy choice."

If policies are focused on exonerating, rehabilitating, and supporting the public, then algorithms will also exonerate, rehabilitate, and support the public. If policies are in place to punish the public, then algorithms will do just that.

"That human choice can sometimes get tech-washed, which gets people thinking the algorithm is saying 50 percent of people are dangerous and should not be released on bail, but in fact, what it reflects is this human policy judgment that a certain number of people must be locked up and held without bail," Bhandari said. "Algorithms in the criminal justice system disguise those choices."

Algorithms and AI have been scientific veneers for racism in government, policing, and the criminal justice system. Technology is not separate from us; it is a part of us, created by us. The problems in technology only exist because of us. How do we separate the longstanding practice of over-policing communities of color and the bias of the algorithm that sent police to those neighborhoods? How would we go about separating the overrepresentation of Black and Latinx people in mugshot databases from the facial recognition systems that rely on this data?

"In the criminal legal system, the problem is not just with the AI systems and the outputs," Bhandari said. "It's what we're asking the AI to do, which result in fundamentally discriminatory or biased outcomes."

If we are capable of building machines that uphold the constructed reality of racism and white supremacy, then we are also capable of designing tools that better reflect the complete and representative reality.

Ultimately, if we hold technology to the lofty goal of ushering in a hopeful and optimistic future, then we need to interrogate the use cases of this technology. Decisions about how technology is used is just as important as decisions about whether technology should be used at all.

HOW IS THIS TECHNOLOGY BUILT?

Our world is becoming more diverse each day. The data used to train algorithms should reflect that. From a business perspective, diverse and representative training data can improve consumers' experience when using a product. For instance, people of color using facial recognition to unlock their smartphones will encounter less identification errors if that feature was exposed to more diverse facial images.

The reason this question should probably come after understanding the technology's impact on different groups and its purpose is because answers to those questions may inform how we evaluate the design of the technology.

For example, if certain ethnic or gender identities are underrepresented in training data, accuracy will suffer. Alternatively, depending on the context, overrepresentation can be a reliable indicator of a discriminatory purpose. What comes to mind is the overrepresentation of Black and Latinx people in mugshot databases and DNA databases. Because police disproportionately target and arrest Black and Latinx people, their inclusion in these databases is also disproportionate.

In both cases, I would argue the flaw is the result of human design or policy decisions, not solely a technology failure. Skewed training data is an oversight in the design process and the overrepresentation of Black and Latinx people in law enforcement databases has more to do with racist policing practices than a technical issue.

Another consideration at this stage should also be *who* is building the technology. The composition of the design and development team provides some insight into the priorities of a company as well as the ability of the team to account for different user experiences.

IF WE DEPLOY THIS TECHNOLOGY, DO THE BENEFITS JUSTIFY THE COSTS?

You might be thinking to yourself, *Well, what about all the benefits of this technology?* I had those same thoughts too. Isn't facial recognition helping the police to solve cold cases? Don't we want algorithms to at least predict the likelihood that a suspect's DNA was at the crime scene?

"When people say that they've used this technology in certain cases, that doesn't mean that they wouldn't have solved the cases without that technology," S.T.O.P. founder Albert Cahn pointed out. "It also doesn't mean that those cases are more than a handful of outliers among a sea of false matches and discriminatory outcomes."

Cahn doesn't believe we've seen enough evidence there is a net benefit for surveillance technology. "We don't know how often surveillance technology gets it wrong. We don't know how often it's putting people in harm's way, of being arrested, detained, or even having a SWAT team show up at the door."

When discussing the cost of surveillance technology, it is important to remember it is truly a matter of life and death because that is the consequence for so many Americans when they have interactions with law enforcement.

While there are certainly benefits to AI, even when it is flawed, it's important to consider what must be traded to enjoy that benefit.

"The benefits are part of what makes it so dangerous," Cahn said. "It allows us to ignore the costs by focusing on these narratives of how the technology will solve all of our issues. If there wasn't some sort of upside for this invasion of our privacy and erosion of our autonomy, they would never be able to implement these technologies to begin with."

* * *

We are living in exciting and terrifying times. AI is flawed and it is already everywhere. There are many activists and organizations dedicated to making technology more accountable, more transparent, and, most importantly, safer.

For instance, the Algorithmic Justice League holds workshops and creates educational materials to raise public awareness about the dangers of AI. Data for Black Lives brings together activists, organizers, and academics committed to using data science to improve Black lives and protest against unethical uses of data. Organizations like the ACLU, the Electronic Frontier Foundation (EFF), and the Surveillance Technology Oversight Project (S.T.O.P.) use litigation and policy advocacy to defend civil liberties and change our public institutions.

This brief list is by no means exhaustive. There are plenty of ways to get involved. It just starts with awareness of the problems and a willingness to improve the current state of affairs.

My goal when I decided to write this book was to bring awareness to this issue and hopefully equip more people with the means to find points of entry for pushing back against irresponsible and malicious actors in the technology space. My hope is, in reading this book, you have acquired a greater awareness of how pervasive and troubling technology can be, as well as how history informs the way this technology is being used today.

A lot of these issues may seem political, but viewing it as such creates distance between the problem and us. This is a matter of privacy, autonomy, and safety. These are personal issues.

One way or another, our response to the widespread use of biased technologies will determine whether hard-won civil liberties endure or become forgotten relics. We have been at the mercy of "innovators" and "disruptors" for too long. The tech industry continues to create, market, and sell flawed products as long as only certain groups are impacted. The government tolerates these flaws so it can continue to rely on private-sector technology to augment the police and surveillance state. The fight against biased technology will require the same energy as any other fight against systems of oppression.

If we are not willing to reflect on the effects of our history, then our technology will simply continue to mirror our past mistakes. History will be doomed to repeat itself, but it will also become increasingly more challenging to see that. We cannot let that future come to pass.

Acknowledgments

———

In creating this book, I had the unique opportunity to interview many different people in the legal and tech fields. Each conversation expanded my understanding and curiosity. The following individuals made this book possible by inspiring me with the work they do and taking the time to share their insights with me:

Renée Cummings, an AI criminologist, AI ethicist, and the first data activist in residence at the University of Virginia's School of Data Science.

Jay Stanley, a senior policy analyst with the ACLU's Speech, Privacy, and Technology Project, where he researches, writes, and speaks about technology-related privacy and civil liberties issues and their future.

Jennifer Granick, the surveillance and cybersecurity counsel with the ACLU's Speech, Privacy, and Technology Project and author of *American Spies: Modern Surveillance, Why You Should Care, and What to Do About It.*

Daniel Kahn Gillmor (DKG), a senior staff technologist for the ACLU's Speech, Privacy, and Technology Project, focused on the way our technical infrastructure shapes society and impacts civil liberties.

Esha Bhandari, a deputy director of the ACLU's Speech, Privacy, and Technology Project, where she works on litigation and advocacy to protect freedom of expression and privacy rights in the digital age. She also focuses on the impact of big data and artificial intelligence on civil liberties.

Aaron Horowitz, a computer scientist and chief data scientist at the ACLU.

Albert Fox Cahn, the founder and executive director of the Surveillance Technology Oversight Project (S.T.O.P.), former fellow at the Engelberg Center on Innovation Law & Policy at NYU School of Law, and a visiting fellow at Yale Law School's Information Society Project.

Vera Eidelman, a staff attorney with the ACLU's Speech, Privacy, and Technology Project, where she works on litigation and advocacy to protect freedom of speech and privacy rights in the digital age.

Rebecca Wexler, a law professor at UC Berkeley School of Law, where she teaches, researches, and writes on issues concerning data, technology, and criminal justice.

Clinton Hughes, a forensic DNA attorney at the Brooklyn Defender Services and a former DNA Unit attorney at the Legal Aid Society.

Richard Torres, a criminal defense attorney and former DNA Unit attorney at the Legal Aid Society.

Frank Pasquale, a law professor at Brooklyn Law School and expert on the law of artificial intelligence, algorithms, and machine learning.

Jerome Greco, a public defender in the Digital Forensics Unit of the Legal Aid Society and Community Advisory Board Member of S.T.O.P.

Sudha Jamthe, the CEO of IoTDisruptions.com and a globally recognized technology futurist.

Clare Garvie, a senior associate with the Center on Privacy & Technology at Georgetown Law and lead author on three of the Center's reports on face recognition: *The Perpetual Line-Up, Garbage In, Garbage Out*, and *America Under Watch*.

Brandon del Pozo, a postdoctoral researcher at Brown University who served nineteen years in the NYPD and four as the chief of police in Burlington, Vermont.

Nate Wessler, a deputy director with the ACLU's Speech, Privacy, and Technology Project, where he focuses on litigation and advocacy around surveillance and privacy issues, including government searches of electronic devices, requests for sensitive data held by third parties, and uses of surveillance technologies.

Brett Max Kaufman, a senior staff attorney in the ACLU's Center for Democracy, where he works primarily on national security issues.

Juyoun Han, a partner in Eisenberg & Baum's Artificial Intelligence Fairness and Data Privacy practice group.

Liz O'Sullivan, the CEO of a new algorithmic fairness company first incorporated by Dr. Rumman Chowdhury called Parity and previously a cofounder of Arthur, an AI model monitoring company.

Thank you to my family for their encouragement and enthusiasm for this passion project.

Thank you to my partner Carly J. Goldberg for her constant love, support, and thoughtful opinions—and for always reminding me to sleep.

Thank you, Eric Koester, Cassandra Caswell-Stirling, and John Chancey for encouraging me, guiding me, and keeping me accountable through this entire process. This would not have been possible without you.

Thank you to those who believed in me and supported my journey by preordering my book. Your encouragement and feedback mean the world to me.

Adam Bindas, Adam Knowles, Adam Zeloof, Ahmed Yousef, Allen Chi, Amanda Stelma, Andrew Loizides, Angel Li, Ankit Kayastha, Anna Meh Feindt, Ashley Shin, Ashley Wang, Beau LaManna, Becky Celestina, Beihong Hu, Benjamin

Kloenne, Brent Lin, Brenton Autler, Brian Brown, Brian Connor, Brittany Sigler, Brooke Buonauro, Bryant Y. Wang, Cameron Moody, Carly Goldberg, Carole White-Connor, Carolina Charvet, Catherine Kim, Cecily D'Amore, Charles Liu, Christian Stallings, Christina Nashed, Chynna Foucek, Claudia Herbert Colfer, Cleo Kordomenos, Cristina Lang, Cynthia Forck, Dan Keesey, Daniel Bashir, Daniel Liberman, Deborah Teslyar, Denise L. Elliot, Desiree Jung, Edward Leung, Elizabeth Jung, Elizabeth Olson, Emily Li, Eric Chi, Eric Koester, Eric Marion, Francine Leung, Frank Cuccio, Gary Chen, Gerald Lam, Gregory Chang, Gus Ipsen, Henry Lin, Jake Smith, Jan Song, Javier Cardenas, Jennifer Kim, Jenny Kuh, Jenny Ryoo, Jerome Greco, Jessica Lanning, Jessie Rong, Jewel Ngatunyi, Joel Marcus, Johana Borjas, Jonathan Lin, Joseph Murphy, Julia Caruso, Juliet Sato, Juyoun Han, Kaman Hung, Karen Lin, Kelli Komorowski, Kelly Corbett, Kelly Yu, Kelsey Carew, Ken Jung, Ken Lin, Kimberly Wright, Kiren Kadekoppa, Krishna Varre, Kyle Gulsby, Laura Horvath-Roa, Lauren McDonough, Leanna Zhan, Lillian Liao, Lily Li, Loren Naftali, MacKenzie Olson, Matthew Stanley, Michael Cederblom, Michelle Lam, Miko Yoshida, Mindy Li, Moriah Son, Moshe Wander, Nathan Kung, Nayef Al Rayes, Neelesh Lalwani, Newton Yu, Nicholas Hollingsworth, Nicole Wolf, Noelle Stone, Norman Zhao, Patcharin Reynolds, Paul McHugh, Pravin Matthew, Priyadarshini Das, Punica Bhardwaj, Rachel Fikslin, Reza Yassi, Rhea Goveas, Sean Liu, Shane Dizon, Sharen Hau, Shreya Tewari, Stacey Lin, Stephanie Lee, Stephanie Quappe, Stephanie Ranque, Sudha Jamthe, Sukhman Bhurjee, Teri Solomko, Tom McHale, Victor Leung, Victoria Kammerath, Xinxin Zhou, Yaroslav Radtsevich, and Yen Jung.

Appendix

———

INTRODUCTION

Bornstein, Aaron. "Are Algorithms Building the New Infrastructure of Racism?" *Nautilus*, December 21, 2017. https://nautil.us/issue/55/trust/are-algorithms-building-the-new-infrastructure-of-racism.

Burkeman, Oliver. "The Power Broker: Robert Moses and the Fall of New York by Robert Caro Review – A Landmark Study." *The Guardian*, October 23, 2015. https://www.theguardian.com/books/2015/oct/23/the-power-broker-robert-moses-and-the-fall-of-new-york-robert-caro-review.

Caro, Robert A. "The Power Broker I–The Best Bill-Drafter in Albany." *The New Yorker*, July 14, 1974. https://www.newyorker.com/magazine/1974/07/22/the-power-broker-i-the-best-bill-drafter-in-albany.

Census Bureau. "New York - Race and Hispanic Origin for Selected Large Cities and Other Places: Earliest Census to 1990." Accessed September 7, 2021. https://www2.census.gov/library/working-papers/2005/demo/pop-twps0076/nytab.pdf.

Gratz, Roberta Brandes. "Robert Moses: Reconsidered: Mostly Right the First Time." *City Limits*, February 12, 2007. https://citylimits.org/2007/02/12/robert-moses-reconsidered-mostly-right-the-first-time/.

Gross, Terry. "A 'Forgotten History' of How the US Government Segregated America." *NPR*, May 3, 2017. https://www.npr.org/2017/05/03/526655831/a-forgotten-history-of-how-the-u-s-government-segregated-america.

Schindler, Sarah. "Architectural Exclusion: Discrimination and Segregation Through Physical Design of the Built Environment." *Yale Law Journal* 124, no. 6 (2015): 1836-2201. https://www.yalelawjournal.org/article/architectural-exclusion.

Stieglitz, C.M, photographer. "Sponsor of Battery Bridge / World Telegram & Sun photo by C.M. Stieglitz." New York, 1939. Photograph. https://www.loc.gov/item/2006675178/.

Williams, Keith. "How Lincoln Center Was Built (It Wasn't Pretty)." *The New York Times*, December 21, 2017. https://www.nytimes.com/2017/12/21/nyregion/how-lincoln-center-was-built-it-wasnt-pretty.html.

CHAPTER 1: FRANGLEN'S MONSTER

Angwin, Julia, Jeff Larson, Surya Mattu, and Lauren Kirchner. "Machine Bias." *ProPublica*, May 23, 2016. https://www.propublica.org/article/machine-bias-risk-assessments-in-criminal-sentencing.

Funk, McKenzie, "How ICE Picks Its Targets in the Surveillance Age." *The New York Times*, October 2, 2019. https://www.

nytimes.com/2019/10/02/magazine/ice-surveillance-deportation.html.

Hao, Karen. "What Is AI? We Drew You a Flowchart to Work It Out." *MIT Technology Review*, November 10, 2018. https://www.technologyreview.com/2018/11/10/139137/is-this-ai-we-drew-you-a-flowchart-to-work-it-out/.

Kraus, Rachel. "What Is an Algorithm, Anyway?" *Mashable*, August 30, 2020. https://mashable.com/article/what-is-an-algorithm.

Mayson, Sandra G. "Bias In, Bias Out." *Yale Law Journal* 128, no. 8 (June 2019): 2218-2300. https://www.yalelawjournal.org/article/bias-in-bias-out.

Myers, Andrew. "Stanford's John McCarthy, Seminal Figure of Artificial Intelligence, Dies at 84." *Stanford News*, October 25, 2011. https://news.stanford.edu/news/2011/october/john-mccarthy-obit-102511.html.

Schwartz, Oscar. "Untold History of AI: Algorithmic Bias Was Born in the 1980s." *IEEE Spectrum*, April 15, 2019. https://spectrum.ieee.org/untold-history-of-ai-the-birth-of-machine-bias.

Sharkey, Noel. "Alan Turing: The Experiment That Shaped Artificial Intelligence." *BBC News*, June 21, 2012. https://www.bbc.com/news/technology-18475646.

Tomlinson, Zachary. "Artificial Entertainment: A Century of AI in Film." *Interesting Engineering*, November 3, 2018. https://

interestingengineering.com/artificial-entertainment-a-century-of-ai-in-film.

CHAPTER 2: AUTOMATING BIAS

Algorithmic Justice League. "Take Action." Accessed May 10, 2021. https://www.ajl.org/.

Barr, Alistair. "Google Mistakenly Tags Black People 'Gorillas,' Showing Limits of Algorithms." *The Wall Street Journal*, July 1, 2015. https://www.wsj.com/articles/BL-DGB-42522.

Buolamwini, Joy. "When the Robot Doesn't See Dark Skin." *The New York Times*, June 21, 2018. https://www.nytimes.com/2018/06/21/opinion/facial-analysis-technology-bias.html.

Day, Matt. "How LinkedIn's Search Engine May Reflect Gender Bias." *The Seattle Times*, August 31, 2016. https://www.seattletimes.com/business/microsoft/how-linkedins-search-engine-may-reflect-a-bias/.

Hao, Karen. "This is how AI bias really happens—and why it's so hard to fix." *MIT Technology Review*, February 4, 2019. https://www.technologyreview.com/2019/02/04/137602/this-is-how-ai-bias-really-happensand-why-its-so-hard-to-fix/.

Mac, Ryan. "Facebook Apologizes After A.I. Puts 'Primates' Label on Video of Black Men." *The New York Times*, September 3, 2021. https://www.nytimes.com/2021/09/03/technology/facebook-ai-race-primates.html.

Mayson, Sandra G. "Bias In, Bias Out." *Yale Law Journal* 128, no. 8 (June 2019): 2218-2300. https://www.yalelawjournal.org/article/bias-in-bias-out.

Papillon, Kimberly. "Bias and Well-Meaning People." Georgetown University Center for Child & Human Development. Accessed April 1, 2021. https://nccc.georgetown.edu/bias/module-3/1.php.

Reflective Democracy Campaign. "System Failure: What the 2020 Primary Elections Reveal about Our Democracy." May, 2021. https://wholeads.us/wp-content/uploads/2021/05/reflectivedemocracy-systemfailure-may2021.pdf.

Tversky, Amos and Daniel Kahneman. "Judgment under Uncertainty: Heuristics and Biases." *Science* 185, no. 4157 (1974): 1124-1131. doi: 10.1126/science.185.4157.1124.

Vincent, James. "Twitter Taught Microsoft's AI Chatbot to Be a Racist Asshole in Less than a Day." *The Verge*, March 24, 2016. https://www.theverge.com/2016/3/24/11297050/tay-microsoft-chatbot-racist.

West, Sarah Myers, Meredith Whittaker, and Kate Crawford. "Discriminating Systems: Gender, Race, and Power in AI." *AI Now Institute*, April 2019. https://ainowinstitute.org/discriminatingsystems.pdf.

Yagoda, Ben. "The Cognitive Biases Tricking Your Brain." *The Atlantic*, September 2018. https://www.theatlantic.com/magazine/archive/2018/09/cognitive-bias/565775/.

CHAPTER 3: LIGHTS, CAMERA, SURVEILLANCE!

Ansfield, Bench. "How a 50-Year-Old Study Was Misconstrued to Create Destructive Broken-Windows Policing." *The Washington Post*, December 27, 2019. https://www.washingtonpost.com/outlook/2019/12/27/how-year-old-study-was-misconstrued-create-destructive-broken-windows-policing/.

Armour, Jody D. "How Being 'Tough on Crime' Became a Political Liability." *The Conversation*, December 20, 2019. https://theconversation.com/how-being-tough-on-crime-became-a-political-liability-128515.

Berlatsky, Noah. "Blade Runner's Source Material Says More about Modern Politics than the Movie Does." *The Verge*, October 5, 2017. https://www.theverge.com/2017/10/5/16428544/blade-runner-philip-k-dick-do-androids-dream-of-electric-sheep-analysis-adaptation.

Bratton, William J. and Sean Malinowski. "Police Performance Management in Practice: Taking COMPSTAT to the Next Level." *Policing-an International Journal of Police Strategies & Management* 2, no. 3 (September 2008): 259-265. https://doi.org/10.1093/police/pano36.

Coates, Ta-Nehisi. "Moynihan, Mass Incarceration, and Responsibility." *The Atlantic*, September 24, 2015. https://www.theatlantic.com/politics/archive/2015/09/moynihan-mass-incarceration-and-responsibility/407131/.

NAACP. "Criminal Justice Fact Sheet." Accessed April 21, 2021. https://naacp.org/resources/criminal-justice-fact-sheet.

Garcia-Rojas, Claudia. "The Surveillance of Blackness: From the Trans-Atlantic Slave Trade to Contemporary Surveillance Technologies." *Truthout*, March 3, 2016. https://truthout.org/articles/the-surveillance-of-blackness-from-the-slave-trade-to-the-police/.

Geary, Daniel. "The Moynihan Report: An Annotated Edition." *The Atlantic*, September 14, 2015. https://www.theatlantic.com/politics/archive/2015/09/the-moynihan-report-an-annotated-edition/404632/.

Getlin, Josh, and Carla Rivera. "Bratton's Plans for Homeless Debated." *Los Angeles Times*, October 31, 2015. https://www.latimes.com/archives/la-xpm-2005-oct-31-me-nyhomeless31-story.html.

Kelling, George L., and James Q. Wilson. "Broken Windows." *The Atlantic*, March 1982. theatlantic.com/magazine/archive/1982/03/broken-windows/304465/.

Olukotun, Deji Bryce. "Sweep, Harvest, Gather: Mapping Metaphors to Fight Surveillance." *The Millions*, April 10, 2014. https://themillions.com/2014/04/sweep-harvest-gather-mapping-metaphors-to-fight-surveillance.html.

NYCLU. "Stop-and-Frisk in the de Blasio Era." March 14, 2019. https://www.nyclu.org/en/publications/stop-and-frisk-de-blasio-era-2019.

Surico, John. "Omnipresence Is the Newest NYPD Tactic You've Never Heard Of." *Vice*, October, 24, 2014. https://www.vice.

com/en/article/vdpq7m/omnipresence-is-the-newest-nypd-tactic-youve-never-heard-of-1020.

Wagner, Peter, and Wanda Bertram. "What Percent of the US Is Incarcerated? (And Other Ways to Measure Mass Incarceration)." Prison Policy Initiative. January 16, 2020. https://www.prisonpolicy.org/blog/2020/01/16/percent-incarcerated/.

Zimbardo, Philip G. "The Human Choice: Individuation, Reason, and Order versus Deindividuation, Impulse, and Chaos." In *Nebraska Symposium on Motivation*, edited by William J. Arnold, and David Levine, 237-307. University of Nebraska Press, 1969. https://stacks.stanford.edu/file/gk002bt7757/gk002bt7757.pdf.

CHAPTER 4: CLOUDY CRYSTAL BALL: PREDICTIVE POLICING

Ahmed, Maha. "Aided by Palantir, the LAPD Uses Predictive Policing to Monitor Specific People and Neighborhoods." *The Intercept*, May 11, 2018. https://theintercept.com/2018/05/11/predictive-policing-surveillance-los-angeles/.

Akpinar, Nil-Jana, Maria De-Arteaga, and Alexandra Chouldechova. "The Effect of Differential Victim Crime Reporting on Predictive Policing Systems." ACM FAccT. March 2021. https://nakpinar.github.io/diff_victim_crime_rep.pdf.

AI Now Institute. "Artificial Intelligence in Criminal Law and Its Use by the Police and Judicial Authorities in Criminal Matters." February 20, 2020. https://ainowinstitute.org/ainow-eu-parliament-libe-committee-written-testimony.pdf.

Babuta, Alexander, and Marion Oswald. "Data Analytics and Algorithmic Bias in Policing." Royal United Services Institute for Defence and Security Studies. September 16, 2019. https://www.gov.uk/government/publications/report-commissioned-by-cdei-calls-for-measures-to-address-bias-in-police-use-of-data-analytics.

Brown, JPat. "PredPol Manual Offers a Look into the World of Policing Pre-crime." *MuckRock*, July 11, 2018. https://www.muckrock.com/news/archives/2018/jul/11/predpol-manual/.

Centre for Data Ethics and Innovation. "Report Commissioned by CDEI Calls for Measures to Address Bias in Police Use of Data Analytics." September 16, 2019. https://www.gov.uk/government/publications/report-commissioned-by-cdei-calls-for-measures-to-address-bias-in-police-use-of-data-analytics.

Ferguson, Andrew Guthrie. "Predicting Policing and Reasonable Suspicion." *Emory Law Journal* 62, no. 2 (2012): 259-325. https://scholarlycommons.law.emory.edu/elj/vol62/iss2/1.

Fried, Ina. "Report Blasts Palantir for Ice Work, Trump Ties." *Axios*, August 8, 2019. https://www.axios.com/report-blasts-palantir-for-ice-work-trump-ties-c34f28bb-de81-4273-bb89-520188535228.html.

Grossman, Lev, Mark Thompson, Jeffrey Kluger, Alice Park, Bryan Walsh, Claire Suddath, Eric Dodds, Kayla Webley, Nate Rawlings, Feifei Sun, Cleo Brock-Abraham, and Nick Carbone. "The 50 Best Inventions." *Time*, November 28, 2011. http://content.time.com/time/subscriber/article/0,33009,2099708-13,00.html.

Haymarket Books. "Policing Without the Police: Race, Technology and the New Jim Code." July 8, 2020. Video, 1:32:51. https://youtu.be/tfonEQTLwo4.

Heaven, Will Douglas. "Predictive Policing Algorithms Are Racist. They Need to Be Dismantled." *MIT Technology Review*, July 17, 2020. https://www.technologyreview.com/2020/07/17/1005396/predictive-policing-algorithms-racist-dismantled-machine-learning-bias-criminal-justice/.

Ibarra, Nicholas. "Santa Cruz Becomes First US City to Approve Ban on Predictive Policing." *Los Angeles Times*, June 23, 2020. https://www.latimes.com/california/story/2020-06-26/santa-cruz-becomes-first-u-s-city-to-ban-predictive-policing.

Miller, Leila. "LAPD Will End Controversial Program That Aimed to Predict Where Crimes Would Occur." *Los Angeles Times*, April 21, 2020. https://www.latimes.com/california/story/2020-04-21/lapd-ends-predictive-policing-program.

Moravec, Eva Ruth. "Do Algorithms Have a Place in Policing?" *The Atlantic*, September 5, 2019. https://www.theatlantic.com/politics/archive/2019/09/do-algorithms-have-place-policing/596851/.

Office of Juvenile Justice Delinquency Prevention Statistical Briefing Book. "Estimated Number of Arrests by Offense and Race, 2019." November 16, 2020. https://www.ojjdp.gov/ojstatbb/crime/ucr.asp?table_in=2.

Price, Michael, and Emily Hockett. "Palantir Contract Dispute Exposes NYPD's Lack of Transparency." Brennan Center for Justice. July 20, 2017. https://www.brennancenter.org/our-work/analysis-opinion/palantir-contract-dispute-exposes-nypds-lack-transparency.

Puente, Mark. "LAPD Ends Another Data-Driven Crime Program Touted to Target Violent Offenders." *Los Angeles Times*, April 12, 2019.https://www.latimes.com/local/lanow/la-me-laser-lapd-crime-data-program-20190412-story.html.

The Berkman Klein Center for Internet & Society. "What is 'Dirty Data?'" April 30, 2019. Video, 1:00. https://www.youtube.com/watch?v=zCZnK16R-Qc.

Uchida, Craig D., Marc Swatt, Dave Gamero, Jeanine Lopez, Erika Salazar, Elliott King, Rhonda Maxey, Nathan Ong, Douglas Wagner, and Michael D. White. "The Los Angeles Smart Policing Initiative: Reducing Gun-Related Violence through Operation LASER." *US Department of Justice, Office of Justice Programs*, October 2012. https://bja.ojp.gov/sites/g/files/xyckuh186/files/media/document/losangelesspi.pdf.

Winston, Ali. "Palantir Has Secretly Been Using New Orleans to Test Its Predictive Policing Technology." *The Verge*, February 27, 2018. https://www.theverge.com/2018/2/27/17054740/palantir-predictive-policing-tool-new-orleans-nopd.

CHAPTER 5: SMILE! YOU'RE ON CAMERA: VIDEO SUR-VEILLANCE

Amadeo, Ron. "The NYPD Retires 'Digidog' Robot after Public Backlash." *Ars Technica*, April 30, 2021. https://arstechnica.com/gadgets/2021/04/the-nypd-retires-digidog-robot-after-public-backlash/.

Electronic Frontier Foundation. "Automated License Plate Readers (ALPRs)." Accessed June 2, 2021. https://www.eff.org/pages/automated-license-plate-readers-alpr.

Carney, Matthew. "Leave No Dark Corner." *ABC News*, July 31, 2020. https://www.abc.net.au/news/2018-09-18/china-social-credit-a-model-citizen-in-a-digital-dictatorship/10200278?section=world&nw=0.

Bridges, Lauren. "Amazon's Ring Is the Largest Civilian Surveillance Network the Us Has Ever Seen." *The Guardian*, May 18, 2021. https://www.theguardian.com/commentisfree/2021/may/18/amazon-ring-largest-civilian-surveillance-network-us.

The Ethics Centre. "Ethics Explainer: The Panopticon." July 18, 2017. https://ethics.org.au/ethics-explainer-panopticon-what-is-the-panopticon-effect/.

He, Huifeng. "China's Social Credit System Shows Its Teeth, Banning Millions from Taking Flights, Trains." *South China Morning Post*, February 18, 2019. https://www.scmp.com/economy/china-economy/article/2186606/chinas-social-credit-system-shows-its-teeth-banning-millions.

Helmore, Edward. "New York Mayor Calls off 'Creepy, Alienating' Police Robo-Dog." *The Guardian*, April 30, 2021. https://www.theguardian.com/us-news/2021/apr/30/new-york-mayor-creepy-police-robo-dog.

Kantayya, Shalini, director. 2020. *Coded Bias*. 7th Empire Media.

Kelley, Jason. "Amazon's Ring Enables the Over-Policing Efforts of Some of America's Deadliest Law Enforcement Agencies." Electronic Frontier Foundation. July 2, 2020. https://www.eff.org/deeplinks/2020/07/amazons-ring-enables-over-policing-efforts-some-americas-deadliest-law-enforcement.

Lee, Amanda. "What Is China's Social Credit System and Why Is It Controversial?" *South China Morning Post*, August 9, 2020. https://www.scmp.com/economy/china-economy/article/3096090/what-chinas-social-credit-system-and-why-it-controversial.

Lin, Liza and Newley Purnell. "A World With a Billion Cameras Watching You Is Just Around the Corner." *The Wall Street Journal*, December 6, 2019. https://www.wsj.com/articles/a-billion-surveillance-cameras-forecast-to-be-watching-within-two-years-11575565402?mod=hp_listb_pos1.

Metz, Cade. "Police Drones Are Starting to Think for Themselves." *The New York Times*, December 5, 2020. https://www.nytimes.com/2020/12/05/technology/police-drones.html.

Ocasio-Cortez, Alexandria. *Twitter*, February 25, 2021. https://twitter.com/aoc/status/1365023067769098245?lang=en.

Palin, Megan. "China's 'Social Credit' System Is a Real-Life 'Black Mirror' Nightmare." *New York Post*, September 19, 2018. https://nypost.com/2018/09/19/chinas-social-credit-system-is-a-real-life-black-mirror-nightmare/.

Tokson, Matthew. "The Emerging Principles of Fourth Amendment Privacy." George Washington Law Review 88, no. 1

(January 2020): 1-75. https://www.gwlr.org/the-emerging-principles-of-fourth-amendment-privacy/.

Wang, Xinyuan. "Hundreds of Chinese Citizens Told Me What They Thought about the Controversial Social Credit System." *The Conversation*, December 17, 2019. https://theconversation.com/hundreds-of-chinese-citizens-told-me-what-they-thought-about-the-controversial-social-credit-system-127467.

Zaveri, Mihir. "N.Y.P.D. Robot Dog's Run Is Cut Short after Fierce Backlash." *The New York Times*, April 28, 2021. https://www.nytimes.com/2021/04/28/nyregion/nypd-robot-dog-backlash.html.

CHAPTER 6: AI SPY WITH MY LITTLE EYE: FACIAL RECOGNITION

Alba, Davey. "The US Government Will Be Scanning Your Face At 20 Top Airports, Documents Show." *BuzzFeed News*, March 11, 2019. https://www.buzzfeednews.com/article/daveyalba/these-documents-reveal-the-governments-detailed-plan-for.

Buolamwini, Joy. "Artificial Intelligence Has a Problem With Gender and Racial Bias. Here's How to Solve It." *Time*, February 7, 2019. https://time.com/5520558/artificial-intelligence-racial-gender-bias/.

Buolamwini, Joy. "When the Robot Doesn't See Dark Skin." *The New York Times*, June 21, 2018. https://www.nytimes.com/2018/06/21/opinion/facial-analysis-technology-bias.html.

Coltin, Jeff. "Why Everyone is Suddenly Talking about the NYPD Gang Database." *City & State New York*, June 13, 2018. https://

www.cityandstateny.com/articles/policy/criminal-justice/why-everyone-suddenly-talking-about-nypd-gang-database.html.

Cox, Kate. "Facebook Will Pay More than $300 Each to 1.6M Illinois Users in Settlement." *Ars Technica*, January 15, 2021. https://arstechnica.com/tech-policy/2021/01/illinois-facebook-users-to-get-more-than-300-each-in-privacy-settlement/.

Edmondson, Catie. "ICE Used Facial Recognition to Mine State Driver's License Databases." *The New York Times*, July 7, 2019. https://www.nytimes.com/2019/07/07/us/politics/ice-drivers-licenses-facial-recognition.html.

Emerson, Sarah. "Police Are Feeding Celebrity Photos into Facial Recognition Software to Solve Crimes." *Vice*, May 16, 2019. https://www.vice.com/en/article/xwngn3/police-are-feeding-celebrity-photos-into-facial-recognition-software-to-solve-crimes.

Grand View Research. "Facial Recognition Market Size, Share & Trends Analysis Report By Technology (2D, 3D, Facial Analytics), By Application (Access Control, Security & Surveillance), By End-use, By Region, And Segment Forecasts, 2021 - 2028." May 2021. https://www.grandviewresearch.com/industry-analysis/facial-recognition-market.

GAO-16-267. "Face Recognition Technology: FBI Should Better Ensure Privacy and Accuracy." US Government Accountability Office. August, 3, 2016. https://www.gao.gov/products/gao-16-267.

GAO-19-579T. "Face Recognition Technology: DOJ and FBI Have Taken Some Actions in Response to GAO Recommendations to Ensure Privacy and Accuracy, But Additional Work Remains." US Government Accountability Office. June 4, 2019. https://www.gao.gov/products/gao-19-579t.

Garvie, Clare, Alvaro M. Bedoya, and Jonathan Frankle. "The Perpetual Line-Up: Unregulated Police Face Recognition in America." Georgetown Law Center on Privacy & Technology. October 18, 2016. https://www.perpetuallineup.org/.

Garvie, Clare, and Jonathan Frankle. "Facial-Recognition Software Might Have a Racial Bias Problem." *The Atlantic*, April 7, 2016. https://www.theatlantic.com/technology/archive/2016/04/the-underlying-bias-of-facial-recognition-systems/476991/.

Germain, Thomas. "Federal Agencies Use DMV Photos for Facial Recognition. Here's What You Need to Know." *Consumer Reports*, July 8, 2019. https://www.consumerreports.org/privacy/federal-agencies-use-dmv-photos-for-facial-recognition/.

Guliani, Neema Singh. "The FBI Has Access to Over 640 Million Photos of Us Through Its Facial Recognition Database." *ACLU*, June 7, 2009. https://www.aclu.org/blog/privacy-technology/surveillance-technologies/fbi-has-access-over-640-million-photos-us-through/.

Grother, Patrick, Mei Ngan, and Kayee Hanaoka. "Face Recognition Vendor Test (FRVT) Part 3: Demographic Effects." National Institute of Standards and Technology, December 2019. https://doi.org/10.6028/NIST.IR.8280.

Harwell, Drew, and Erin Cox. "ICE Has Run Facial-Recognition Searches on Millions of Maryland Drivers." *The Washington Post*, February 26, 2020. https://www.washingtonpost.com/technology/2020/02/26/ice-has-run-facial-recognition-searches-millions-maryland-drivers/.

Hill, Kashmir. "Meet Clearview AI, the Secretive Company That Might End Privacy as We Know It." *Chicago Tribune*, January 18, 2020. https://www.chicagotribune.com/nationworld/ct-nw-nyt-clearview-facial-recognition-20200119-dkdqz7ypaveb3id42tpz7ymase-story.html.

Hirose, Mariko. "Privacy in Public Spaces: The Reasonable Expectation of Privacy Against the Dragnet Use of Facial Recognition Technology." *Connecticut Law Review* 49, no. 5 (2017): 1591-1620. https://opencommons.uconn.edu/law_review/377/.

Illinois General Assembly. "740 LCS 14 - Biometric Information Privacy Act." Accessed April 20, 2021. https://www.ilga.gov/legislation/ilcs/ilcs3.asp?ActID=3004&ChapterID=57.

Ivanova, Irina. "Why Face-Recognition Technology Has a Bias Problem." *CBS News*, June 12, 2020. https://www.cbsnews.com/news/facial-recognition-systems-racism-protests-police-bias/.

Lynch, Jennifer. *Face Off: Law Enforcement Use of Facial Recognition Technology.* Edited by Gennie Gebhart. Electronic Frontier Foundation, April 2020. https://www.eff.org/files/2020/04/20/face-off-report-2020_1.pdf.

McCullagh, Declan. "Call It Super Bowl Face Scan I." *Wired*, February 2, 2001. https://www.wired.com/2001/02/call-it-super-bowl-face-scan-i/.

Najibi, Alex. "Racial Discrimination in Face Recognition Technology." *Science in the News*, October 24, 2020. http://sitn.hms.harvard.edu/flash/2020/racial-discrimination-in-face-recognition-technology/.

Phillips, P. J., Alice K. O'Toole, Abhijit Narvekar, Fang Jiang, and Julianne Ayadd. *An Other-Race Effect for Face Recognition Algorithms*. National Institute of Standards and Technology, May 13, 2010. https://www.nist.gov/publications/other-race-effect-face-recognition-algorithms-0.

Powers, Benjamin. "Eyes Over Baltimore: How Police Use Military Technology to Secretly Track You." *Rolling Stones*, January 6, 2017. https://www.rollingstone.com/culture/culture-features/eyes-over-baltimore-how-police-use-military-technology-to-secretly-track-you-126885/.

Reuters Staff. "US Tests Bin Laden's DNA, Used Facial ID: Official." *Reuters*, May 2, 2011. https://www.reuters.com/article/us-binladen-dna/u-s-tests-bin-ladens-dna-used-facial-id-official-idUSTRE7411HJ20110502.

Schuppe, John. "How Facial Recognition Became a Routine Policing Tool in America." *NBC News*, May 11, 2019. https://www.nbcnews.com/news/us-news/how-facial-recognition-became-routine-policing-tool-america-n1004251.

Snow, Jacob. "Amazon's Face Recognition Falsely Matched 28 Members of Congress With Mugshots." *ACLU*, July 26, 2018. https://www.aclu.org/blog/privacy-technology/surveillance-technologies/amazons-face-recognition-falsely-matched-28.

US Government Publishing Office. "About Face: Examining the Department of Homeland Security's Use of Facial Recognition and Other Biometric Technologies, Part II." February 6, 2020. https://www.govinfo.gov/content/pkg/CHRG-116hhrg41450/html/CHRG-116hhrg41450.htm.

Valentina-DeVries, Jennifer. "How the Police Use Facial Recognition, and Where It Falls Short." *The New York Times*, January 12, 2020. https://www.nytimes.com/2020/01/12/technology/facial-recognition-police.html.

Williams v. City of Detroit, Detroit Police Chief James Craig, and Detective Donald Bussa, 21-cv-10827 (April 13, 2021). https://www.aclumich.org/sites/default/files/field_documents/001_complaint_1.pdf.

CHAPTER 7: SMOKING GUN OR SMOKE AND MIRRORS: FORENSIC EVIDENCE

Arnaud, Celia Henry. "Thirty Years of DNA Forensics: How DNA Has Revolutionized Criminal Investigations." *Chemical & Engineering News*, September 18, 2017. https://cen.acs.org/analytical-chemistry/Thirty-years-DNA-forensics-DNA/95/i37.

Ahmed, Aziza. "Ethical Concerns of DNA Databases used for Crime Control." Bill of Health. January 14, 2019. https://blog.petrieflom.law.harvard.edu/2019/01/14/ethical-concerns-of-dna-databases-used-for-crime-control/.

The National Registry of Exonerations. "Browse the National Registry of Exonerations." Accessed June 28, 2021. https://www.law.umich.edu/special/exoneration/Pages/browse.aspx.

Cino, Jessica Gabel. "Forensic Evidence Largely Not Supported by Sound Science – Now What?" *The Conversation*, December 6, 2016. https://theconversation.com/forensic-evidence-largely-not-supported-by-sound-science-now-what-67413.

Congress.gov. "H.R.4368 - Justice in Forensic Algorithms Act of 2019." Accessed May 10, 2021. https://www.congress.gov/bill/116th-congress/house-bill/4368/text.

Curley, Lee John, and James Munro. "CSI: Current Research into the Impact of Bias on Crime Scene Forensics Is Limited – But Psychologists Can Help." *The Conversation*, October 29, 2019. https://theconversation.com/csi-current-research-into-the-impact-of-bias-on-crime-scene-forensics-is-limited-but-psychologists-can-help-125467.

DeBenedictis, Don J. "DNA Report Raises Concerns: Study Backs Genetic Evidence, but Questions Reliability of Labs, Statistics." *ABA Journal* 78, no. 7 (July 1992): 20-20. https://www.jstor.org/stable/27830704.

Dror, Itiel E., David Charlton, Ailsa E. Péron. "Contextual Information Renders Experts Vulnerable to Making Erroneous Identifications." *Forensic Science International* 156, no. 1 (January 6, 2006): 74-78. https://doi.org/10.1016/j.forsciint.2005.10.017.

Dror, Itiel E., and Greg Hampikian. "Subjectivity and Bias in Forensic DNA Mixture Interpretation." *Science & Justice* 51, no. 4 (December 2011): 204-208. https://doi.org/10.1016/j.scijus.2011.08.004.

Elster, Naomi. "How Forensic DNA Evidence Can Lead to Wrongful Convictions." *JSTOR Daily*, December 6, 2017. https://daily.jstor.org/forensic-dna-evidence-can-lead-wrongful-convictions/.

Federal Bureau of Investigations. "CODIS – NDIS Statistics." Accessed May 19, 2021. https://www.fbi.gov/services/laboratory/biometric-analysis/codis/ndis-statistics.

MacDonald, James. "How Scientific is Forensic Science?" *JSTOR Daily*, April 2, 2019. https://daily.jstor.org/how-scientific-is-forensic-science/.

Innocence Project. "Overturning Wrongful Convictions Involving Misapplied Forensics." Accessed June 28, 2021. https://innocenceproject.org/overturning-wrongful-convictions-involving-flawed-forensics/.

Shaer, Matthew. "The False Promise of DNA Testing." *The Atlantic*, June 2016. https://www.theatlantic.com/magazine/archive/2016/06/a-reasonable-doubt/480747/.

Committee on Identifying the Needs of the Forensic Sciences Community, National Research Council. *Strengthening Forensic Science in the United States: A Path Forward*. Washington D.C.: National Academies Press, 2009. https://www.ojp.gov/pdffiles1/nij/grants/228091.pdf.

van Oorschot, Roland AH, Kaye N. Ballantyne, and R. John Mitchell. "Forensic trace DNA: A Review." *Investigative Genetics* 1, no. 14 (2010). https://doi.org/10.1186/2041-2223-1-14.

CHAPTER 8: BEYOND A RELATIVE DOUBT: FORENSIC DNA DATABASES & FAMILIAL DNA SEARCHES

Aldhous, Peter. "The Genealogy Website That Helped Crack The Golden State Killer Case Has Been Bought By A Forensic Genetics Firm." *BuzzFeed News*, December 9, 2019. https://www.buzzfeednews.com/article/peteraldhous/the-genealogy-website-that-helped-crack-the-golden-state.

Brand, David. "NYPD Alters How it Collects DNA from Children and Certain Suspects." *Brooklyn Daily Eagle*, February 21, 2020. https://brooklyneagle.com/articles/2020/02/21/nypd-alters-how-it-collects-dna-from-children-and-certain-suspects/.

FBI. "CODIS – NDIS Statistics." Accessed July 20, 2021. https://www.fbi.gov/services/laboratory/biometric-analysis/codis/ndis-statistics.

National Conference of State Legislature. "DNA Arrestee Laws." Updated 2018. https://www.ncsl.org/Documents/cj/Arrestee_DNA_Laws.pdf.

Molteni, Megan. "The Creepy Genetics Behind the Golden State Killer Case." *Wired*, April 27, 2018. https://www.wired.com/story/detectives-cracked-the-golden-state-killer-case-using-genetics/.

Murphy, Erin and Jun H. Tong. "The Racial Composition of Forensic DNA Databases." *California Law Review* 108, no. 6 (2020): 1847-1911. https://doi.org/10.15779/Z381GoHV8M.

Perrin, Andrew. "About half of Americans are OK with DNA testing companies sharing user data with law enforcement." Pew Research Center. February 4, 2020. https://www.pewresearch. org/fact-tank/2020/02/04/about-half-of-americans-are-ok-with-dna-testing-companies-sharing-user-data-with-law-enforcement/.

Federal Register. "Proposed Guidelines for the Jacob Wetterling Crimes Against Children and Sexually Violent Offender Registration Act, as Amended." June 19, 1998. https://www.govinfo. gov/content/pkg/FR-1998-06-19/html/98-16391.htm.

Rainey, James. "Familial DNA Puts Elusive Killers behind Bars. But Only 12 States Use It." *NBC News*, April 28, 2018. https:// www.nbcnews.com/news/us-news/familial-dna-puts-elusive-killers-behind-bars-only-12-states-n869711.

Stanton, Sam. "Relative's DNA from Genealogy Websites Cracked East Area Rapist Case, DA's Office Says." *The Sacramento Bee*, April 27, 2018. https://www.sacbee.com/latest-news/article209913514.html.

Steinberger, Eva, and Gary Sims. "Finding Criminals Through the DNA of Their Relatives—Familial Searching of the California Offender DNA Database." *31 Prosecutor's Brief 1 & 2*, (April 16, 2014). https://ceadstorage.blob.core.windows.net/cead-images/ CDAAfamilialsearcharticle.pdf.

FBI National Press Office. "The FBI's Combined DNA Index System." FBI. May 21, 2021. https://www.fbi.gov/news/pressrel/press-releases/the-fbis-combined-dna-index-system-codis-hits-major-milestone.

Erlich, Yaniv, Tal Shor, Itsik Pe'er, and Shai Carmi. "Identity Inference of Genomic data using Long-range Familial Searches." *Science* 362, no. 6415 (2018): 690-694. doi: 10.1126/science.aau4832.

CHAPTER 9: ALGORITHMS GET THEIR DAY IN COURT

Angwin, Julia, Jeff Larson, Surya Mattu, and Lauren Kirchner. "Machine Bias." *ProPublica*, May 23, 2016. https://www.propublica.org/article/machine-bias-risk-assessments-in-criminal-sentencing.

Bornstein, Aaron M. "Are Algorithms Building the New Infrastructure of Racism?" *Nautilus*, December 21, 2017. https://nautil.us/issue/55/trust/are-algorithms-building-the-new-infrastructure-of-racism.

Carter, Madeline, and Alison Shames. "APPR Statement on Pretrial Justice and Pretrial Assessment." Advancing Pretrial Policy & Research. Accessed May 7, 2021. https://mailchi.mp/7f49d0c94263/our-statement-on-pretrial-justice?e=a01efafabd.

Gambino, Lauren and Ben Jacobs. "Bernie Sanders' Cash Bail Bill Seeks to End 'Modern Day Debtors' Prisons.'" *The Guardian*, July 25, 2018. https://www.theguardian.com/us-news/2018/jul/25/bernie-sanders-cash-bail-bill-seeks-to-end-modern-day-debtors-prisons.

Giorgis, Hannah. "Why It Matters That So Many People Are Donating to Bail Funds." *The Atlantic*, June 6, 2020. https://www.theatlantic.com/culture/archive/2020/06/why-sudden-popularity-bail-funds-matters/612733/.

Grawert, Ames. "What Is the First Step Act – And What's Happening With It?" *Brennan Center for Justice*, June 23, 2020. https://www.brennancenter.org/our-work/research-reports/what-first-step-act-and-whats-happening-it.

Henry, Matt. "Risk Assessment: Explained." *The Appeal*, December 14, 2019. https://theappeal.org/the-lab/explainers/risk-assessment-explained/.

Liptak, Adam. "Illegal Globally, Bail for Profit Remains in US" *The New York Times*, January 29, 2008. https://www.nytimes.com/2008/01/29/us/29bail.html.

Onyekwere, Adureh. "How Cash Bail Works." *Brennan Center for Justice*, last updated February 24, 2021. https://www.brennancenter.org/our-work/research-reports/how-cash-bail-works.

Sawyer, Wendy, and Peter Wagner. "Mass Incarceration: The Whole Pie 2020." Prison Policy Initiative. March 24, 2020. https://www.prisonpolicy.org/reports/pie2020.html.

State v. Loomis, 881 N.W.2d 749, 760-64 (Wisc. 2016).

Tashea, Jason. "Courts Are Using AI to Sentence Criminals. That Must Stop Now." *Wired*, April 17, 2017. https://www.wired.com/2017/04/courts-using-ai-sentence-criminals-must-stop-now/.

The American Law Institute. "Model Penal Code: Sentencing Approved." May 24, 2017. https://www.ali.org/news/articles/model-penal-code-sentencing-approved/.

The PJI Team. "Updated Position on Pretrial Risk Assessment Tools." Pretrial Justice Institute. February 7, 2020. https://www.pretrial.org/wp-content/uploads/Risk-Statement-PJI-2020.pdf.

Villasenor, John and Virginia Foggo. "Algorithms and Sentencing: What does Due Process Require?" *The Brookings Institution*, March 21, 2019. https://www.brookings.edu/blog/techtank/2019/03/21/algorithms-and-sentencing-what-does-due-process-require/.

Wexler, Rebecca. "Life, Liberty, Trade Secrets: Intellectual Property in the Criminal Justice System." *Stanford Law Review* 70, no. 5 (May 2018): 1343-1429. https://www.stanfordlawreview.org/print/article/life-liberty-and-trade-secrets/.

CHAPTER 10: BEHIND CLOSED SOURCE: HOW THE LAW KEEPS ALGORITHMS HIDDEN FROM US

Berk, Richard. *An Impact Assessment of Machine Learning Risk Forecasts on Parole Board Decisions and Recidivism.* University of Pennsylvania, Department of Criminology, July 24, 2016. https://crim.sas.upenn.edu/sites/default/files/WP2016-04_Berk_MachineLearningParole_08.03.2016%281%29.pdf.

Bornstein, Aaron. "Are Algorithms Building the New Infrastructure of Racism?" *Nautilus*, December 21, 2017. https://nautil.us/issue/55/trust/are-algorithms-building-the-new-infrastructure-of-racism.

Brennan, Tim, William Dieterich, and Beate Ehret. "Evaluating the Predictive Validity of the COMPAS Risk and Needs Assessment System." *SAGE Journals: Criminal Justice Behavior* 36, no. 1 (October 20, 2008): 21-40. https://doi.org/10.1177%2F0093854808326545.

Corbett-Davies, Sam, Sharad Goel, and Sandra González-Bailón. "Even Imperfect Algorithms Can Improve the Criminal Justice System." *The New York Times*, December 20, 2017. https://www.nytimes.com/2017/12/20/upshot/algorithms-bail-criminal-justice-system.html.

Heaven, Will Douglas. "Predictive Policing Algorithms Are Racist. They Need to Be Dismantled." *MIT Technology Review*, July 17, 2020. https://www.technologyreview.com/2020/07/17/1005396/predictive-policing-algorithms-racist-dismantled-machine-learning-bias-criminal-justice/.

Henry, Matt. "Risk Assessment: Explained." *The Appeal*, December 14, 2019. https://theappeal.org/the-lab/explainers/risk-assessment-explained/.

Lipton, Beryl. "Idaho Legislators Approve Law Requiring Transparency for Risk Assessment Tools." *MuckRock*, March 26, 2019. https://www.muckrock.com/news/archives/2019/mar/26/algorithms-idaho-bill-update/.

Morgan, Rachel E., and Jennifer L. Truman. "Criminal Victimization, 2017." Bureau of Justice Statistics, December 2018. https://www.bjs.gov/content/pub/pdf/cv17.pdf.

Human Rights Watch. "'Not in it for Justice': How California's Pretrial Detention and Bail System Unfairly Punishes Poor People." April 11, 2017. https://www.hrw.org/report/2017/04/11/not-it-justice/how-californias-pretrial-detention-and-bail-system-unfairly.

Northpointe. "Practitioner's Guide to COMPAS Core." March 19, 2015. http://www.northpointeinc.com/downloads/compas/Practitioners-Guide-COMPAS-Core-_031915.pdf.

State v. Loomis, 881 N.W.2d 749 (Wisc. 2016).

Tashea, Jason. "Courts Are Using AI to Sentence Criminals. That Must Stop Now." *Wired*, April 17, 2017. https://www.wired.com/2017/04/courts-using-ai-sentence-criminals-must-stop-now/.

Thompson, Derek. "Should We Be Afraid of AI in the Criminal-Justice System?" *The Atlantic*, June 20, 2019. https://www.theatlantic.com/ideas/archive/2019/06/should-we-be-afraid-of-ai-in-the-criminal-justice-system/592084/.

Yong, Ed. "A Popular Algorithm Is No Better at Predicting Crimes Than Random People." *The Atlantic*, January 17, 2018. https://www.theatlantic.com/technology/archive/2018/01/equivant-compas-algorithm/550646/.

CHAPTER 11: DIGITAL SHACKLES: HOW PAROLE APPS PUT PRISON IN YOUR POCKET

Anderson, Emma. "The Evolution Of Electronic Monitoring Devices." *NPR*, May 24, 2014. https://www.npr.

org/2014/05/22/314874232/the-history-of-electronic-monitoring-devices.

US Immigration and Customs Enforcement. "Detention Management." September 30, 2020. https://www.ice.gov/detain/detention-management.

Feathers, Todd. "'They Track Every Move': How Us Parole Apps Created Digital Prisoners." *The Guardian*, March 4, 2021. https://www.theguardian.com/global-development/2021/mar/04/they-track-every-move-how-us-parole-apps-created-digital-prisoners.

Jones, Alexi. "Correctional Control 2018: Incarceration and Supervision by State." Prison Policy Initiative. December 2018. https://www.prisonpolicy.org/reports/correctionalcontrol2018.html.

Kilgore, James. *Electronic Monitoring is Not the Answer: Critical Reflections on a Flawed Alternative.* Urbana-Champaign Independent Media Center, October 2015. https://mediajustice.org/wp-content/uploads/2020/01/EM-Report-Kilgore-final-draft-10-4-15.pdf.

Paunescu, Delia. "The Faulty Technology behind Ankle Monitors." *Vox*, December 1, 2019. https://www.vox.com/recode/2019/12/1/20986262/ankle-monitor-technology-reset-podcast.

Solon, Olivia. "'Digital Shackles': The Unexpected Cruelty of Ankle Monitors." *The Guardian*, August 28, 2018. https://

www.theguardian.com/technology/2018/aug/28/digital-shackles-the-unexpected-cruelty-of-ankle-monitors.

The Pew Charitable Trusts. "Use of Electronic Offender-Tracking Devices Expands Sharply." September 2016. https://www.pewtrusts.org/en/research-and-analysis/issue-briefs/2016/09/use-of-electronic-offender-tracking-devices-expands-sharply.

Wolf, Gary. "The Twin Inventors of Electronic Monitoring Still Have Regrets." *Wired*, October 23, 2007. https://www.wired.com/2007/10/ps-ankle/.

CHAPTER 12: FUTUREPROOFING OUR CIVIL LIBERTIES

Locke, Matt. "Data Isn't Oil, So What Is It?" *How To Measure Ghosts* (blog). May 15, 2021. https://howtomeasureghosts.substack.com/p/data-isnt-oil-so-what-is-it.

Naughton, John. "Data Isn't Oil, Whatever Tech Commentators Tell You: It's People's Lives." *The Guardian*, May 29, 2021. https://www.theguardian.com/commentisfree/2021/may/29/data-oil-metaphor-tech-companies-surveillance-capitalism.

CHAPTER 13: THE WILD WILD WEST

Executive Office of the President. "Big Data: A Report on Algorithmic Systems, Opportunity, and Civil Rights." May 2016. https://obamawhitehouse.archives.gov/sites/default/files/microsites/ostp/2016_0504_data_discrimination.pdf.

Congress.gov. "H.R.3103 - Health Insurance Portability and Accountability Act of 1996." Accessed June 10, 2021. https://www.congress.gov/bill/104th-congress/house-bill/3103/text.

Goode, Erica. "Shots Fired, Pinpointed and Argued Over." *The New York Times*, May 28, 2012. http://www.nytimes.com/2012/05/29/us/shots-heard-pinpointed-and-argued-over.html.

Guszcza, James, Iyad Rahwan, Will Bible, Manuel Cebrian, and Vic Katyal. "Why We Need to Audit Algorithms." *Harvard Business Review*, November 28, 2018. https://hbr.org/2018/11/why-we-need-to-audit-algorithms.

Kehl, Danielle, Priscilla Guo, and Samuel Kessler. "Algorithms in the Criminal Justice System: Assessing the Use of Risk Assessments in Sentencing." *Responsive Communities Initiative, Berkman Klein Center for Internet & Society, Harvard Law School*, (July 2017). http://nrs.harvard.edu/urn-3:HUL.InstRepos:33746041.

MacCarthy, Mark. "AI needs more regulation, not less." *The Brookings Institution*, March 9, 2020. https://www.brookings.edu/research/ai-needs-more-regulation-not-less/.

Carbon Disclosure Project. "New Report Shows Just 100 Companies Are Source of over 70% Of Emissions." July 10, 2017. https://www.cdp.net/en/articles/media/new-report-shows-just-100-companies-are-source-of-over-70-of-emissions.

Ng, Alfred. "Can Auditing Eliminate Bias from Algorithms?" *The Markup*, February 23, 2021. https://themarkup.org/ask-the-markup/2021/02/23/can-auditing-eliminate-bias-from-algorithms.

Nocera, Joseph. "The Day the Credit Card Was Born." *The Washington Post*, November 4, 1994. https://www.washingtonpost.

com/archive/lifestyle/magazine/1994/11/04/the-day-the-cred-it-card-was-born/d42da27b-0437-4a67-b753-bf9b440ad6dc/.

Robertson, Adi. "A New Bill Would Force Companies to Check Their Algorithms for Bias." *The Verge*, April 10, 2019. https://www.theverge.com/2019/4/10/18304960/congress-algorith-mic-accountability-act-wyden-clarke-booker-bill-intro-duced-house-senate.

CHAPTER 14: FLIPPING THE SCRIPT: THE ROLE OF THE PRIVATE SECTOR

Clark, Jack, and Gillian K. Hadfield. "Regulatory Markets for AI Safety." *ArXiv* abs/2001.00078 (2020): 1-23. https://api.seman-ticscholar.org/CorpusID:209531921.

Hadfield, Gillian. "An AI Regulation Strategy That Could Really Work." *VentureBeat*, February 8, 2020. https://venturebeat.com/2020/02/08/an-ai-regulation-strategy-that-could-real-ly-work/.

Ho, Daniel E., and Alice Xiang. "Affirmative Algorithms: The Legal Grounds for Fairness as Awareness." *The University of Chicago Law Review Online*, October 30, 2020. https://lawreviewblog.uchicago.edu/2020/10/30/aa-ho-xiang/.

Humerick, Jacob. "Reprogramming Fairness: Affirmative Action in Algorithmic Criminal Sentencing." Columbia Human Rights Law Review. April 15, 2020. http://hrlr.law.columbia.edu/hrlr-online/reprogramming-fairness-affirmative-ac-tion-in-algorithmic-criminal-sentencing/.

Menand, Louis. "The Changing Meaning of Affirmative Action." *The New Yorker*, January 13, 2020. https://www.newyorker.com/magazine/2020/01/20/have-we-outgrown-the-need-for-affirmative-action.

Parents Involved in Community Schools v. Seattle School District No. 1, 551 US 701 (2007).

Reitz, Kevin R., and Cecelia Klingele. *Model Penal Code: Sentencing, Tentative Draft No. 2*. American Law Institute, 2011. https://www.ali.org/publications/show/sentencing/.

Rozen, Courtney. "How Americans Feel About Affirmative Action in Higher Education." *NPR*, November 1, 2018. https://www.npr.org/2018/11/01/658960740/how-americans-feel-about-affirmative-action-in-higher-education.

Schuette v. Coalition to Defend Affirmative Action, Integration and Immigration Rights and Fight for Equality by Any Means Necessary, 572 US 291 (2014).

Skeem, Jennifer L., and Christopher Lowenkamp. "Using Algorithms to Address Trade-Offs Inherent in Predicting Recidivism." *Behavioral Sciences & the Law* Forthcoming, (May 12, 2020). https://papers.ssrn.com/sol3/papers.cfm?abstract_id=3578591.

Urofsky, Melvin I. *The Affirmative Action Puzzle: A Living History from Reconstruction to Today*. New York: Pantheon Books, 2020.

US Equal Employment Opportunity Commission. "Timeline of Important EEOC events." Accessed June 10, 2021. https://www.eeoc.gov/youth/timeline-important-eeoc-events.

US Equal Employment Opportunity Commission. "Title VII of the Civil Rights Act of 1964." Accessed June 10, 2021. https://www.eeoc.gov/statutes/title-vii-civil-rights-act-1964.

CHAPTER 15: BEYOND TECHNOLOGY: EXPECTING MORE FROM AI

Hao, Karen. "We Need to Design Distrust into AI Systems to Make Them Safer." *MIT Technology Review*, May 3, 2021. https://www.technologyreview.com/2021/05/13/1024874/ai-ayanna-howard-trust-robots/.

Jean, Neal, Marshall Burke, Michael Xie, W. Matthew Davis, David B. Lobell, and Stefano Ermon. "Combining Satellite Imagery and Machine Learning to Predict Poverty." *Science* 353, no. 6301 (2016): 790-794. https://doi.org/10.1126/science.aaf7894.

Provine, Robert R. "Faces as Releasers of Contagious Yawning: An Approach to Face Detection Using Normal Human Subjects." *Bulletin of the Psychonomic Society 27*, no. 3 (1989): 211-214. https://link.springer.com/content/pdf/10.3758%2FBF03334587.pdf.

Temple-Raston, Dina. "Elephants Under Attack Have An Unlikely Ally: Artificial Intelligence." *NPR*, October 25, 2019. https://www.npr.org/2019/10/25/760487476/elephants-under-attack-have-an-unlikely-ally-artificial-intelligence.

Made in United States
North Haven, CT
31 March 2023

34840103R00143